BLUEBELL

DIARY OF A CAT

BLUEBELL

DIARY OF A CAT

Jan D'Lord

ILLUSTRATED BY
William Geldart

MICHAEL O'MARA BOOKS LIMITED

First published in Great Britain in 1997 by
Michael O'Mara Books Limited
9 Lion Yard
Tremadoc Road
London SW4 7NQ

A CIP catalogue record for this book is available from the British
Library

ISBN 1-85479-266-0

1 3 5 7 9 10 8 6 4 2

Designed and typeset by K DESIGN, Winscombe, Somerset
Printed and bound in Finland by WSOY

Contents

CONTENTS

To all those who encouraged me . . .
they know who they are.
To Ross for not minding what I write about him.
And to Bluebell . . . for letting me read her mind.

To read a cat's mind is an honour.
To read Bluebell's mind is hilarious.

Foreword

Bluebell is an enigma. Those eyes, so big, so amber, say nothing to most and yet to me say everything. This is where Bluebell wears her heart. But she only allows a glimpse to those who don't know cats. She spills so many secrets about feline relationships that we can all benefit from her diary. Every cat owner will know more than they can explain about how their cat thinks. They will see more than a bit of their own cats in this diary.

I knew Bluebell was, shall we say ... unusual, the day we got her. We had chosen her at three weeks but had to wait until she was big enough to leave her mum before our excitement could be satisfied.

She was barrel-shaped, fluffy and so blue there could never be any other name for her. She also had 'attitude'. Her face made us laugh; if only we'd known how much we'd have done rib-strengthening exercises.

She trotted out of the basket to see her new home and didn't like it. She didn't like us either and made it perfectly clear she didn't think us up to the job. I tried to pick her up for the cuddle I'd waited months to enjoy, but she wasn't having any of it. My hand-span was just enough to hold her round the tummy and in mid-air she made her legs, front and back, scrabble the air. She could do without humans.

She stretched a point at meal times however and proved herself to be a real guzzle-guts.

She might have left was it not for Pussy Willow. Our red-shaded Cameo Persian was sweetness to all. She'd had two litters of kittens, and although she knew Bluebell was not hers, she loved and understood her. Our other cats

Dumpling, Miss Smith and Muffycat all tolerated the self-opinionated whirlwind that had entered Foxgloves, our home for strange cats and stranger people.

It would have been easy to give up on Bluebell as self-centred; many did. But as the older cats fell to their natural fate, Bluebell blossomed.

It was when Bracken the golden retriever bounded into our feline world that I noticed how much Bluebell would let me see past those ever-watching eyes. She spent most of her time on the kitchen work-surfaces to avoid rough puppy play. I made a fuss of her and spent more time at eye level than previously. Once I had glimpsed that chink into her soul, I knew forever what she was thinking.

She tolerated another puppy, Clover, and then Bramble, a foundling kitten who at four weeks had lost her mother. Apart from Willow, Bluebell was now the most senior to all around her. Unknowingly, she opened up further to me and when work forced us to move from Yorkshire to Lincolnshire, her mind went into overdrive.

I could see it all going on in that cute little head of hers. 'Cute' is a word she'd hate me to use. She regards herself as a true beauty, superior in looks and intelligence to everyone, no matter how many legs they have.

Do you know, she's right. Who else could make us laugh so much whilst thinking themselves to be so above it all?

If you love cats you'll love Bluebell's diary. If you love to laugh you'll get great pleasure from these pages. If you love both . . . are you in for a treat!

Bluebell the Resolutionary

1 January

Jenny has threatened me. If I'm as naughty this year as I was last, I'm for it.

'You have to make some New Year resolutions Bluebell, and you have to stick to them otherwise you can carry your own cat food back from the supermarket.'

As I don't even know where the supermarket is I have to have a go. Why should I have to improve myself? If it works, I will be even more superior to everyone else around here! Here's my list:

1 I mustn't scoot a tomato stalk across the kitchen floor, wait for the scream and then accept a reward for being a spider-conquering heroine.
2 I resolve not to treat bare summer knees in the same way as a denim-clad lap when I heave myself up for a cuddle.
3 I will remember not to leave paw-prints or lick-marks on the butter.
4 I will take the blame honestly and not frame the puppies next time I steal a defrosting chicken, break a wine glass, walk through the water bowl . . . .
5 When I dig a hole in the garden I will try not to replant the flowers upside down.
6 I won't wait until Ross has just hoovered before I have an extra good de-tufting session.

7 I will stop punching the puppies on the nose just before I steal their titbits. (Will it be allowed afterwards?)

8 I will stop leaving bits of mouse on the doormat, just where Jenny wanders down barefoot in the mornings.

9 I will learn to speak up when I have licked a dinner plate extra clean and Jenny absent-mindedly puts it back in the cupboard.

10 I will stop beating up Ross's Garfield slippers after a good roll in the catnip.

11 I will try not to sit on the roof of the bird table just after bread, seeds and nuts have been piled on.

12 I'll have a go at not howling and yowling when Jenny's favourite soap-opera comes on the TV (I'll wait until Ross's favourite, the news.)

13 I shouldn't lie on Jenny's glasses when she is searching the house for them.

14 I will move away from the fire *before* I smell burning fur.

15 I promise to limit myself to just *one* wildlife party a week.

16 When I have muddy paws I will not: walk across the bonnet of the newly washed car; squash through the sun roof; walk across those white lace cushions on the white lace bedspread.

17 I will not wait until the phone rings or until the potatoes are almost cooked before I jump on to Jenny's knee to give her the cuddle she's been asking for all day.

18 I will do as Ross suggests and get myself a pet so I can learn how much hard work it involves. A pretty ladybird or a nice quiet hairy worm I think.

19 I promise not to pretend I don't like tinned food when I know there are prawns in the fridge.

20 I will give up clawing my way upside down beneath the bed, or under the duvet for a quick bite of Ross's toes or full length up his naked body to chew his hair.

21 I will try to give up jumping between them in bed for a vigorous all-over lick at three in the morning. (What's wrong with slurping and jiggling anyway?)

This is getting ridiculous! How can I live? There is nothing else to do.

How can I stick to those rules *and* have fun?

I think I'll scrap all the above and just have one good resolution: I WON'T GET CAUGHT!

Happy New Year and don't be too good, it's boring!

A Moving Experience

10–12 January

I came back from holiday and they'd moved! The cheek! The injustice of it all has motivated me to tell you just what I think. What a trick! All those years I'd spent finding and fighting for the sunniest spots in the village. All those mouse-holes I had sussed and all those toms I had tamed. All gone. I'll have to start over. But first I am going to make sure as many people as possible know what I have to put up with in living with these people who call themselves animal lovers!

I'm starting on that horrible day when I found out that they tell me nothing. I had wondered why I had been left at Jenny's friend's cottage in Yorkshire for a week. Usually, Pussy Willow, the pinkish blonde Persian, and Bramble, the RSPCA foundling tabby, and me are bundled off to a cattery, but being the middle of the holiday season all must have been full. We didn't mind, Linda and Keeley hadn't had cats before so they left chickens to defrost on the table overnight, meat pies to cool at jumping height and white lace cushions within flinging distance of a muddy garden. It was great.

I had thought the journey home was longer than usual – I went to sleep in Yorkshire and woke up in Lincolnshire! I knew none of the trees in the garden and none of the rooms in the house. Only the sofas and beds were familiar but even they were in silly positions, piled with boxes and clothes.

I didn't like it. I wasn't staying.

I made for the door but Jenny caught me.

'Now Bluebell I hope you aren't going to be awkward.' She knew by the look on my face that I was, so she shut me in a bedroom with my basket and food bowls – the red ones I last licked in Yorkshire.

One by one other cats and other baskets were edged in around a slightly opened door followed by a flash of Jenny's blonde head as she took the quickest look possible. We jumped on to the windowsills. I wondered where the puppies were. Bracken is so eager to please with her golden retriever head-tilt and I-adore-you look, and Clover is copying her in a way all owners of black labradors will know and drool over. I could see them going mad in the big garden. *They* could be trusted. They would slobber over Jenny and Ross wherever they lived.

Next morning Jenny looked me in the eye and decided to keep all the doors shut.

Everyone here was so busy painting the new house and arranging furniture that I hadn't been stroked for four hours. It wasn't until I heard the new doorbell, a horrible dinging I'd never get used to, that I saw my chance. As Jenny took the flowers I ran through her legs, then past those of an unsuspecting florist.

I was mad and legged it off up the road to find my old home.

That Jenny might be too fat, but she soon overtook me at a stile where she grabbed me with such ferocity you'd have thought I was a criminal. I yowled and screamed but she held me by the scruff as she jiggled back to the house.

The doors were then locked.

I had to get my own back.

Next morning, I heard her get up, put the kettle on and shake the biscuit box. I was starving but revenge would feed me. I heard the other cats munch and crunch but I stayed where I was. It was so unusual for me not to appear for breakfast that I heard Jenny's shaky voice as it woke Ross.

'I can't find Boobies! She's gone! Eaten by a fox! Stolen or runover!'

I didn't fancy any of those. I was glad I was hiding. I saw her pull on her leggings before she ran outside. Hair sticking up, eye make-up smudged on her cheeks and not a bit of lip-gloss in sight! I ask you. Eight o'clock on a Sunday morning running around the village shouting 'Booby-Woobies! Blooby! Bluebellllll!'

I felt ashamed. All those people doing Sunday morning stuff being woken and annoyed by a screaming Estée Lauder reject. She shouted over gardens, coo-eed through barns and ran the full length of the main road. When she finally panted back, she bashed Ross with the news-papers for letting me out when he'd sneaked out for his sly cigarette the night before.

Still I hid.

I got the old treatment of mince-wrapping rattled around the house and a tin of tuna was opened to waft temptation to my nostrils. Willow and Bramble went wild with desire, but I stayed where I was. I heard furniture being moved, newly-arranged clothes were thrown from cupboards and she walked past me twice. Then I saw it! A terrified bloodshot eye met mine at the tiny crack between two wardrobes.

'AIYYYYYYEEEEEEEEE!!!!!!'

My ear-drums almost split.

'She's dead! She's dead! Fallen down there and lain in pain all night. I'll never forgive myself!'

This was even better than I'd anticipated. All I'd done was jump from the windowsill to the top of one wardrobe and then slid down the right-angled gap. Actually, I'd spent the night on

the bed in perfect comfort and only just made it between the wardrobes when it got light.

Muscle-man Ross moved the furniture and calmed down the screaming mad woman.

I didn't come out. I waited for the feel of trembling hands on my fur before I stuck out my chin and allowed myself to be kissed and stroked.

I got mince, tuna and some cream. It pays to play hard to get. That'll teach them to move! But if this standard of feasting keeps up I might, only might, consider settling.

I'll have a look around tomorrow. BURP! Oops! When I've slept off all this food.

New Smells
for Old

15 January

I am to be trusted.

Today, three days after moving, that dirty trick Jenny and Ross played on me behind my back, and *they* are trusting *me*!

They think I don't know the way home but I do. I don't know how I know, I just do. Jenny says this is home now because this is where they live. OK, they brought my stuff but I was happy in Yorkshire; just because Ross found a new way to make money doesn't mean *my* life has to be disrupted.

I decided to play along. Jenny made great efforts to keep us cats happy with comfy things and tasty bits. She even gave extra cuddles but I don't like the way she smells of paint and dust. It's worse than that perfume stuff she gets out of her dressing-table drawer. I'd never tell her this but I like her to smell just of her. I love to lick her nose when she's just woken, and she smells heavenly after a couple of hours digging the garden.

We were promised a little sortie outside. About time too! Three days of looking out of the window at those trees made my claws tingle for a good rake at stout bark.

I felt a bit shy. I don't know what came over me but when the kitchen door was opened I didn't rush out as I had dreamed I would. I kept my feet on the terracotta tiles and stuck my head into the breeze. I sniffed. I could detect

four-day-old tomcat but nothing since. The puppies had their uses.

Bramble and Willow were behind me saying I was causing a jam. I gave them a look that let them know it was for their own interest. I didn't want them to tumble into danger. Bramble shot me a 'Cissy' look so I ambled down the step on to toe-poking gravel. The others dashed past me, whizzed across the patio and flung themselves around the lawn like toy aeroplanes on a string.

Where is their dignity? What squashed their caution and our shared plans for when we got out of that box-room prison?

Clover and Bracken bounded up from behind a clump of trees at the bottom of the garden. They joined in the madness that was flinging furry bodies around the grass like a D-day celebration.

I stayed where I was. I had a decision to make. Would I stay or would I make good use of that mental map in my mind?

Jenny came up behind me just then and what she said changed my life. She could have told me how much she loved me, how she would spare no effort in making me secure and safe, how she would cosset and care for me and hold me close. For a moment I thought she'd take me in her arms and carefully carry me around the garden introducing me to every shrub and tree so that all the monsters in my mind would be quietened. But no. She put her slippered foot under my bottom and pushed.

'Bluebell get out there and play. Stop being a big girl's blouse!'

What an attitude!

So! She didn't care if I legged it back to the next county. I'll show her I thought, she's not getting rid of me that easily. I'm staying put!

But I might make a meal of it and stay out late. She deserves another scare. Doesn't do to let her get too sure of me.

Naughty Stuff

23–24 January

Inever thought the new year would mean new trouble. Suddenly nothing is safe, relaxed or clean. The cause of my worst nightmare has doubled! As if we didn't have enough fur in this house, Jenny has now brought two kittens into our scatty but comfortable lives.

Farthing and Dandelion are two striped monsters as far as I am concerned, but Jenny calls them 'babies' and cuddles them to within an inch of their lives.

The puppies and cats who already live here, thank you very much, are all ambushed and chewed. The new kittens learned very early on that I would take no nonsense and so have proceeded to try to remove most of my hair, eat my food and dig at my bed.

Farthing is the cheekiest, he's had several swings on the iron flex, he's been in the washing machine, the fridge, the oven, the dishwasher and every bed. He climbs up legs whether or not they are clothed, he pounces on the duvet monsters and hasn't yet realised they are Jenny's feet. I won't tell him; let him make a fool of himself.

Dandelion just hides behind the bed and under the desk. He is a scaredy-cat when people are around but when they've gone out he is pretty bright. He is learning from Farthing who goes around with a permanent look on his face which says, 'Any naughty stuff for me to do in here?

Don't bother, I've spotted a couple of things.' Those keep him busy for a few minutes and then he thinks of things even I never thought about.

No one showed him the cat-flap: he just looked out, whizzed through and sauntered back with a leaf in his mouth. He did this ten times before he realised they weren't alive, it was just a windy day. Jenny blamed me for the mess as up till now I've been the naughtiest.

Jenny keeps coming back from the shops with some weird things she calls toys. There is a stick with pink feathers and tinsel spouting from the top. We all laughed and thought it was a fairy wand she would use to make Ross disappear.

I knew Farthing wouldn't like it as he is pretty tough. I was wrong.

The moment he saw it his eyes went bright, he jumped, grabbed and almost turned himself inside out with delight. Once he clamped his little jaws on to those fluffy bits he wouldn't let go . . . even for a prawn! It was dragged around the kitchen, heaved up the stairs and guarded with his life. It will be a life-long companion . . . if he doesn't tear it to shreds.

Meanwhile all us cats and puppies have unwillingly become fond of our little intruders. Not that we have any choice. We are bombarded with big ears and little paws, tiny teeth and wobbling, fat little bodies.

This house is bedlam, pink feathers everywhere. Nothing is safe, especially me. They think I am either a cushion or a trampoline.

Jenny says kittens should come with their own vacuum cleaner. She is right of course but she forgot to add mop and bucket, damp sponge, disinfectant, touch-up paint and toy box.

I need nothing, just food and the occasional rub (which is all I get anyway). I am no bother – cheap to keep! We all are. But these kittens cost a fortune and wreck the house.

I sometimes wonder if it is their plan to ruin everything we have. They are making a good job of it anyway. Ross thinks they will grow out of it, but once a hooligan, always a tearaway. They seem to think one good tear deserves another. You should see the bed in Jenny's study! It is just a little bed with blue and white flowery covers and chirpy little teddies making the most of plump cushions. Perfect. Or it used to be. Jenny thinks it still is but she should get on that tummy of hers to check, it is torn to shreds underneath and there must be a whole tree's worth of leaves there too. Jenny took the drawers out so that Dandelion who was so shy when he arrived could crawl underneath and feel secure.

Does ripping give a sense of security? If so, Dandelion must be most confident by now. The leaves are still Farthing's contribution to the chaos but they both splatter food everywhere. And when are they going to abandon a litter tray for heaven's sake? It is a monstrosity in our beautiful home and I keep getting little granules between my toes. It isn't hygienic.

I thought that, since they respected me as a sort of grown-up, a paragon of virtue, I would show them how not to be dependent on artificial aids. Do you know Dandelion was actually coming in from the garden to use the tray! Can you believe it? All that soil and the paddock and he runs to the house, bangs through the flap and scatters litter everywhere. I blocked the flap one day, just sat there blobbing out.

He crossed his legs and mewed. I wasn't as soft as Jenny, he wasn't getting his own way. He jumped into a plant pot and dug furiously but not half as furiously as Jenny would shout when she saw all the compost scattered across the patio. I jumped up there, too, so I could get him off. Of course that was when Jenny came around the corner and blamed me.

'Bluebell, after all these years, I can't believe my eyes!' I couldn't believe mine either; Dandelion was nowhere to be seen. How does he do that?

I tried running but the shock had me at a disadvantage. I had to take the decibels. On and on she went about plants and mess and dirty paws. I was heaved into the kitchen, had my paws dabbed with a dishcloth that had obviously just wiped an onion-cutting knife, and got shut in the utility room. The cat-flap was locked. All I had was a bowl of water and a litter tray. I ignored them both for as long as I could but in the end I drank which in course led me to the tray. How undignified!

I tried to write 'Bluebell is innocent!' in the litter but it was too loose, the sides of the letters I made with my paws just kept caving in and in the end it read: 'lloololl io innooool.' It made me look a fool so I rubbed it out.

She shuts her eyes as well as her nose when she empties the tray, so she wouldn't have read my plea anyway. I wiggled in the litter to smooth out my work and she came in then.

'Oh Bluebell you are dim. It is for weeing in not for sleeping in. Out you go.'

It wasn't any consolation that the puppies and cats all tried to be nice to me, for they didn't stay long. After all, who wants to lie beside a Persian cat whose paws smell of onions?

Wet Weekend

1–3 February

Iknow some cats like to swim but they're foreign and they're certainly not *me*.

The only time I allow my lovely paws to get wet is when I want the kitchen to myself and flick drinking water all over the others. Willow is so dopey she thinks it's raining and runs up to a bedroom.

Can you imagine my horror then when we cats were left alone for an afternoon and a pipe burst in the kitchen. First I knew was when a rocking motion woke me as my basket floated gently past the cooker on its way to the fridge. I was half a metre above the floor along with soggy cream crackers and swimming tea-bags.

The water was gushing from a cupboard and hurling tins of soup (cream of tomato), and jars of jam and peanut butter right at me. I looked down to see them sink to the bottom as their labels floated to the top. Being so fat, I had to hold tight. If I sunk, would my beautiful well-groomed fur float to the top? I didn't want to find out. I wanted dry land and I wanted it quick!

The door was open and my basket was gathering speed. Unfortunately, my cushion was also gathering water; I could see it glistening around the edges. The thought of my lovely little bottom getting damp was horrifying.

I grabbed at the door frame as I sailed past, but the basket wobbled so dangerously I was forced to keep still. I was heading for the cat-flap. Water was gushing out there.

Clunk! I've never seen above the cat-flap before but now I was eye to eye with the letter-box. The water beneath me started to swirl, I felt sick.

Claws out, I made a very daring leap at that brush thing that stops draughts (and sometimes letters) from entering our home. I had to use all my strength and considerable cunning to cling on. I could hear my basket banging against the door until . . . silence. It sank to the new carpet that had been fitted the week before.

Fear swung me to the telephone table from where I made an Olympic leap for the stairs. The flood had reached the fourth tread. I had landed on the fifth. I heard laughter from above. Willow and Bramble and the kittens were sniggering. I lifted my head proudly and began to groom myself as if I was calm and in control. Inside my heart was rattling like a washing machine at full speed.

From the garden I heard a shriek. Jenny had returned. Two heaves and a shove later the door opened and the water level dropped quickly.

'Bluebell, is this your fault? Just look at you!'

I turned round and saw my tail was sodden and dripping.

Willow looked so pleased that I was in trouble that I flicked my tail to shower her silly face. She ran upstairs muttering something about never seeing so much rain.

I demanded all my meals upstairs, refusing to come down until I was sure my gorgeous paws would never get wet again.

Two days later I was very hungry; they were all too busy mopping and tearing up carpets even to consider my needs. After my powerful miaow, Jenny grabbed the tin opener, then thrust a dish of fruit cocktail before me. It took five goes at tins which had lost their labels before I got my meaty chunks.

Pancake Daze

11 February

Are pancakes meant to be worn on the head? I don't think so!

Jenny does. She thought it was very funny and of course she was the one who did it . . . put one on *my* head. It was more of a toss actually, she is getting worse. Why would anyone spend ages mixing flour, eggs and milk together until the mixture was lump free (quite an achievement for her I can tell you), cook this as thinly as possible and then toss it up and down with their tongue sticking out?

She said it was Shrove Tuesday.

What? Is that as bad as Black Wednesday?

Only for me. It was black beneath that pancake but thankfully not too hot. It was her practice pancake and the flame had long been turned out beneath the unfortunate piece of batter.

She was having guests and this is what she was feeding them – pancakes for heaven's sake!

Now I don't know how others are brought up but I don't think you ask people to dress up, drive for miles, give you bottles of expensive wine and bunches of flowers and then feed them pancakes. I will die of embarrassment when they come.

I suppose it was my fault that I got a splat on the head. The puppies and kittens had all become bored with Jenny's tossing about and had gone out for an hour, hoping things would be normal when they returned.

In this house?

Never!

I had sat there, watching. There was a remote possibility I would get something to eat at the end of all that smoke. If I did, it wouldn't be her first attempt. Many pancakes looked scrambled or burnt – others were definitely not pan shaped, and none could be described as a cake.

Until suddenly, it happened.

Jenny got excited and brushed me away when I tried to show how pleased I was by stretching up the cooker.

'Watch out Bluebell, I'm going for it!'

She stood back, gripped the pan with two hands, shook it back and forth and then made a loud grunt before throwing the contents into the air and actually catching it back in the pan.

I was full of admiration and would have been impressed had she not performed again . . . and again . . . and again.

Now correct me if I'm wrong, but is the tossing more important than the eating? I don't think so!

I must admit it was interesting, if only for the many positions her tongue took to help in her search for perfection.

But when the pancake hit my head, I was cross. Not just because I couldn't see or because I was covered in grease but because she laughed. Then she made it worse by not removing my unwanted 'blanket' when Ross suddenly appeared home from work.

'Hi,' he said louder than the kiss which I knew from experience would have hit her cheek. 'You haven't made any yet?'

She must have pointed to me because he laughed.

'Grey furry legs for a pancake filling? Mind if I pass!'

They laughed even harder then, and you know what they did next?

Took photos.

How could they! They will probably add them to that album in which they have just put some photos of us, like the one where Clover as a puppy held on to Bracken's tail when they were running for a stick, and the one of Willow after she'd fallen in the pond.

They made no effort to free me from my floppy prison, and if the puppies hadn't been attracted by their laughter and run in, I might have stayed like that for weeks.

Usually I don't like cold noses and rubbery lips too close to me but this time I was glad that Bracken and Clover were so greedy.

I tried to summon all my dignity as I walked disdainfully away. But it was hard with oil-slicked hair.

As I turned the corner I heard a second burst of laughter. I was glad they found it so funny.

Well, they won't be laughing when their guests arrive and they discover I knocked over that big jar of cream they'd bought specially. The puppies didn't seem to mind that they'd had their pancake before the filling.

Horrible Heart

14 February

I've had a Valentine's card.

Don't laugh but I didn't know what it was.

I only knew that Jenny ran to the post today and opened everything addressed to Ross. She let out a sigh of relief when there was nothing but bills. Funny because usually that upsets her.

She came over to me as I was licking at a particularly hard-to-reach bit of fur and waved an envelope above me.

'Secret lover, Bluebell? Who do you know in Devon?'

What was she on about now?

She showed me the pink and blue flowers adorning this thing and said it must be from an admirer. Well that's a hard one, I have millions of those. I have a very good pedigree you know.

Like Ross, I never get to open my own letters. The only one I have addressed to me is from the vet telling me it's time for my annual injections. If I knew when that was coming I'd rip it to shreds before Jenny even got it. This however, was a new one.

She sniffed at it which was the first sensible thing I saw her do that day. 'Mmmm! Lovely,' she smiled. If she'd been a cat she would have known then who had sent me the thing, but no; she has to open the envelope. She took out a card which had a big red heart on the front with a golden arrow piercing it.

It looked horrible! It was hate mail!

Who would send me a card like that? It was effective – I felt wounded.

'Cheer up Bluebell,' Jenny said when she saw my face – she's nothing if not sensitive. 'It's flattering to receive a Valentine.'

I didn't find the promise of being prepared for a barbecue flattering. What a funny woman Jenny was.

'There is a message Bluebell, just for you.'

I jumped from the table then, I didn't want to hear of skewering and piercing. She gathered me up and whispered in my ear:

'Noses are red,

Bodies are blue.

Without it being said,

I've fallen for you.'

What?

Who had fallen, and where from and to? Why were they sending me a card telling me this? Anyway my nose isn't red, it's the sweetest shade of grey you ever saw.

'Ahhh, Bluebell, isn't that lovely? Someone is in love with you.'

Stupid!

I sniffed the envelope then; the smell would hold more clues than that gobbledegook. It smelt of chemicals from a plastic bottle like those ones Jenny rubs into her hands when she's been gardening. I opened my mouth slightly and let my brain work this one out.

It reminded me of that old lady who came to stay at Christmas. The mother-in-law who used to tell Ross how to do everything. She had loads of bottles and jars of chemicals on the dressing table when she was visiting here. This one was hers. It was how her hands always smelt.

I was pleased then, she was so nice to me – let me sleep on the bed *without* kicking and complaining. I always got some of her breakfast bacon and she never sent me back when I went for a walk with her and the dogs. She was right about the nose too, it was red all the time she was here. She kissed it every morning and we wore the same lipstick all day.

I was pleased she loved me, but why did she send me a pierced heart? That was a bit sick!

Jenny saw I wasn't convinced.

'The heart is hers Bluebell, and the arrow represents love for you which has entered it. It is quite charming.'

If that is charming, I am glad I am not a member of the human race.

If she'd wanted to impress me, why didn't she send me a pound of liver or some fresh giblets?

Waste of money, Valentines. I had to look at it all day on the dresser.

When Ross came home she'd disposed of the envelope and pretended the card had been sent to her.

Ross was upset and spent the rest of the night being extra nice to her.

More than her nose will be red when he learns the truth.

Robin's Revenge

17–20 February

Farthing has caught his first bird!
I tried in vain to warn him but like all males he takes no notice. Needs to learn the hard way.

He had been sitting under the bird table for a few hours every day since he and Dandelion arrived at Ha'penny Hollow. I nudged and pushed him away loads of times and told him he'd be for it if Jenny saw him but he growled. Nobody growls at me, kitten or no kitten. I bashed him in the mouth.

After that I was dying for him to get caught. Every time he settled down for a hide-and-spring session I tried to attract Jenny's attention so she would give him what for.

I patted the window but she told me off.

'I've just cleaned those Bluebell! Get your mucky paws off.'

I tried screaming right beside him as he was being showered with breadcrumbs but that made him run away and I got told off for intimidating sparrows.

As if!

Next time I scooted through the flap and ran straight to the french windows to show her what he was doing but she only took one eye off morning TV long enough to open the window and stupidly I went out through it.

One day I spent the whole morning on her knee staring pointedly out of the window at the bird table. She took a little interest.

'What is it Bloobies, want to learn to fly?' She laughed

but didn't look out to see a naughty kitten wiggling his bottom at a chatter of starlings.

I lost interest then. Let him get on with it. Only I hoped I'd be out when that piercing scream hit the ceiling.

I wasn't!

It shot straight through my ears, clearing any brains as it went.

It was worse than I remember. When I caught a bird she shouted so loud and threw me out so swiftly that I have never even looked at a bird in her presence since, except from the other side of glass.

If she comes into the garden suddenly and I am watching birds pecking around from my place on the garden bench, I look up, then down, then I study my nails. I manage to look nonchalant when she approaches and put my entire heart, soul and limpid eyes into a look that says, 'Birds? What birds? Were there any birds?'

It works now, it's how I gained her trust.

I wish I hadn't been asleep when the scream shattered through the universe. That made it worse for me, but what

made it worse for Farthing was the fact he'd caught a robin. Jenny is very fond of robins as they sing every sunny morning and give her a good mood to get up in. She believes if you feed the birds all winter they'll sing for you all the rest of the year. This limp little body would sing no more. I knew from what followed that that would be the first and last bird Farthing ever caught in his jaws.

He was chased round and round the sofa dangling what he thought of as a great prize from his clamped jaws. He had never had anything but loving encouragement from Jenny's voice and he couldn't believe his oversized ears. She was bellowing and telling him he was bad. He didn't know what bad was but he knew he didn't like this foaming monster wearing Jenny's clothes but not wearing her usual smile.

She grabbed his body and shook it. He dropped the robin and Jenny picked it up tenderly. She apologised to the ruffled red breast and the dull eyes. She loved it with her voice and berated Farthing with a sound he realised came from the same person.

That's when he got the message. He will never kill again. It seared through to his soul that Jenny might not love him.

She held the bird tenderly and told Farthing 'NO. NO!'

It was the first time he had heard that word, but he knew what it meant.

She wouldn't cuddle him for the rest of the day so I became the big object of Jenny's attentions. He came up to her knee twice and purred at me. I ignored him. He had to learn.

Secretly my heart was breaking for he looked so miserable. If he had known the way back to the Cats' Protection League he would have taken it. But he didn't, so he went outside and brought in a decaying leaf which he laid at Jenny's feet. She thought he'd had enough and picked him up. He snuggled beside me and almost purred his head off with relief.

'Why didn't you tell me, traitor?' he breathed into my fur.

I knocked him off the settee then. Quite roughly. Jenny made no fuss as he went into the garden again. She knew he'd never re-offend. Only she didn't know what I knew.

I waited a couple of minutes for word to get around and then I went to the breakfast table in the kitchen. The view of the bird table is unrivalled there and I am allowed to watch the birds from behind the glass. Farthing was near the table but facing away, looking at anything but birds. That is how they got him.

An enormous cock pheasant with red cheeks and chest appeared from the badger wood and swooped at the kitten from behind. One peck of the ear was all it took. The bird was quickly left alone to gobble his reward of sunflower seeds and corn.

His 'karrk-karrk' was triumphant as he flew off knowing he'd done his bit for birds everywhere. I'm glad I wasn't out there. He was bigger than me and much more effective in the 'just watch it' department.

I don't know who he got it from but he had a definite look in his eye that said 'I'LL BE BACK!'

Bad Hair Day

1 March

I have had a biscuit stuck on my head all day.
No one told me. Everyone laughed.

Can you imagine someone of my breeding, someone who is of a higher status than most average cats, having to walk around trying to command attention and respect with a soggy old biscuit snuggling into the fur just in front of my left ear?

I had dived into the breakfast bowl as usual before Jenny finished shaking the box. Everyone does it; it's a matter of pride to get the first crunch of the day and I don't like to be beaten. It was Saturday and for some reason Jenny and Ross didn't get up as early as normal so I was licking my fur to perfection when I heard the thump of feet and the drag of curtains. I had just moistened that hard-to-reach bit which needs to have wet-paw cleaning. All was abandoned in the race downstairs dodging tartan slippers and dangling cords.

As always I focused on the first biscuit to hit the dish and got it. The price for that is often a hail of brown stars to waken the brain. I'm used to it but I have never had to wear breakfast all day. I sat on the step in the sun, did aerobics on the car bonnet and even posed for a passer-by's photo (she was really snapping our remarkable catkin tree but I never let the opportunity for a photo shoot pass me by).

I enjoyed a game of ping-pong with Willow and Bramble and showed my exacting skills with a pencil to the kittens. The puppies stopped chewing an old slipper on the lawn to

admire my balance on the garden wall and I did notice they seemed happier than usual. I know now that they were suppressing laughter. They had made a pact with everyone else just to let me look like a fool all day.

I only noticed my strange hair adornment when I woke after a sleep on the front windowsill. Four visitors had come to the door and I hadn't stirred when I heard their usual admiration. I woke and stretched, just catching a glimpse of my reflection in the window. I thought I had a growth, then an attached bumble-bee taking revenge for all the summer chasing and pouncing I do. I bent slightly to take a better look and jumped sky high, it looked exactly like something horrible from outer space.

That leap made it fall to the windowsill and one sniff told me that this piece of goo had once been a crunchy tasty bit of food. I pushed it around a bit in disgust and did my 'Come here this minute!' yowl.

I heard paws and shoes running from the kitchen but it was the paws that got there first. Bracken slobbered and gobbled the biscuit leaving a large wet tongue-slurp on the shiny wood.

'Are you all right Bluebell?' Jenny gushed, her eyes falling on me first, then the puddle.

'You horrible little girl!' she yelled pushing me to the ground. 'How dare you make such a mess when the cat-flap is so near.'

The indignity of such a false accusation has not yet left me. I am hatching a plan of revenge. It involves melted chocolate, bubblegum and crushed cornflakes.

Let the others talk their way out of that one. I'll have the perfect alibi.

Tat Attack

5–6 March

Watch out there's a comb about! . . . And scissors and a brush.

I'm off behind the settee. I know what's next! It'll be the motorbike gloves and the steely determination.

'Right Bluebell, you are tatty enough. I'm going to give you a spring clean. De-tuft every inch of your fat little body.'

Every March it's the same. Jenny remembers all too well that March when my usually gorgeous coat became so matted and lumpy it cost her £30 at the vet's.

I was as ashamed as she was to admit that I looked like a neglected orphan. She blamed me for running off at the sound of the drawer which hides worming pills, flea powder and the dreaded grooming kit. On the other paw, I blame her. If she can't bear the occasional protest and yowl, she shouldn't have such a treasure as a long-haired cat.

A rough tongue can only do so much. Fur balls have never been a favourite of mine. Jenny tries to brush me every day but I'm too quick for her. Anyway she pulls enough hair from me to stuff a cushion.

I wouldn't put it past her to make a profit by selling cushions made plump by the world's most beautiful cat.

Willow has even longer hair than me but like all blondes gets away with murder. She lets that wide-toothed comb glide over her body every morning and there are no tats. Me? I'm too busy doing clever stuff and finding new and exciting adventures.

I've reached some of my top speeds for exiting through

the cat-flap when that comb appears. Jenny used to chase me and soon got to know every hiding place. She only had to wait until the rattle in my tummy made me rattle at the flap and she pounced.

I would be grabbed, held down by Ross who pretended to be nice by giving me a chin rub, then it would start. That awful ripping noise as my lovely grey hair resisted steel teeth. I would give the first growl low in my chest. That had Jenny working faster. Then, as soon as I felt the scissors sawing through a lump, I would go for the ear-piercing yowl. Two wriggles and a paw flay later and I was off . . . .

Personal hair care is a priority for me but so is having the upper hand. I'm the boss and the sooner those people realise it the better.

Yesterday, when I was fluffing up my new hair-do as I sat on the garden wall, a car drew up. I have never seen such a shine on metal before, but there was more to come. A sweet-smelling lady got out of the car with her golden-haired daughter. 'Oh look Annabelle,' she said with ever such a posh voice. 'Isn't this just the sweetest cat you ever saw!'

I arched my back and gave that head-on-one-side cute look which always gets me what I want. Long, red finger-nails raked over my head and into that spot behind my ears. I could see diamonds flashing on both hands and I don't know where this lady bought her clothes but it certainly wasn't at the same shop where Jenny gets those smelly, torn canvas jackets.

This pair oozed class and money.

'Do you think the pussykins is lost mummy. Can we take her home?'

I looked down into a face of pure love. Prawns, chicken and a life of luxury flashed before my eyes.

I mewed my loudest 'YES PLEASE!' I expected to be clutched to that expensive bosom and driven away to para-dise but that was not what happened.

There was a slam of the door and a yell from the tatti-est, lumpiest Jenny I'd ever seen.

'What is going on?' she screeched. She had a threadbare

GELDART

bath robe over a soup-stained sweatshirt; tartan slippers bobbed pompoms around the bottom of bare, white legs.

'That's *my* Booby-Woobies.'

I wanted to evaporate. The shame of belonging to such a scarecrow, even if she had rushed straight from preparing for a shower to rescue me.

I tried to look terrified as if I'd never seen this awful creature before, hoping the rich lady would save me. But no! I was grabbed, thrust roughly under Jenny's arm and had my ear blasted.

'There is a law against taking special cats you know!'

'We'd like to buy her from you.'

I was all for it and wondered how much commission I'd get. But I was out of luck and Jenny was out of breath.

'Never, she's the world to me!'

Well, Jenny's world was having the life squeezed out of it.

My wealthy admirers got back into their expensive car and glided away. Jenny went into the shower and I went into a huff.

It would have been nice to be rich and pampered, and not squashed . . . even if I did have to answer to 'pussykins'.

Uncovering a Stink

11 March

What on earth are potting sheds for?

Pottering about in, right! Well that's all I was doing. Honest! I know I'm not supposed to go in, but a half-open door into somewhere a cat has never been before is like winning the lottery. I felt the excitement grow as my eyes widened. It was dark, spidery and full of places to stick your nose.

Ecstasy!

No wonder they never potter in there, there isn't any room. Jenny had filled a big bowl with bird seed, sunflower seeds and peanuts from sacks spilling out on to the floor. Believe it or not some things actually eat this stuff. No wonder birds are so little, no meat! She had kicked the door shut behind her but it didn't catch as the winter had swollen the wood. It was the creak as it opened again behind her back which attracted me. It sounded sort of sinister and interesting. It suggested something naughty and I love naughty.

My eyes quickly adjusted to the dimness and my fur seemed to find a new purpose in life as it gathered cobwebs at every little twist and turn. I didn't mind. I could sort out my appearance later. Right now there was mystery and I love that too.

The biggest mystery, however, seemed to be how they

ever got all this stuff in the first place. It was a dump for all the boxes from things they'd bought in the last twenty years, broken stuff and objects too ugly for words. I started on the first floor. That Jenny had built a skyscraper but it had no real structure, just a 'toss it and hope' kind of plan.

There were lots of places to set my paws as nothing stacked up like the pyramids. But I knew there was unearthed treasure beneath those blocks she'd dragged from electrical shops and supermarkets in town.

I squeezed into a box marked 'This Way Up'; it wasn't of course.

It seemed to have housed a TV in its youth, but now the worn and wrinkled cardboard had the indignity of being crammed with thin romantic novels. They all had paper sticking out where Jenny had marked the juicy bits. It was a bit squashy so I climbed even further. Do you know what was in the one above? Every bit of china in that nasty tartan pattern that Ross's aunty had been giving them every Christmas for years.

On the same level, but at an angle, was a cosy box full of woolly jumpers all stiff like a bull's ear. Jenny washes everything on hot! No doubt they were awaiting the miracle reversal-cure Jenny was sure some mad scientist would invent. She should know, she shares his mental state.

I was getting high now and not just from the climb. There was something stinky up there. I nosed towards it, quite literally. The shock of arrival quite unsteadied me.

I put a paw wrong and slipped. I managed to hold on for a few seconds but I could feel the box, damp from weeks of winter rain, tear and give way.

I reached the bottom before the books and before the woollies, thankfully, for they shielded me from the bad-taste china. Quite efficiently I thought for such battle-scarred cardigans.

She heard the smashing.

'Bluebell!!! I had those all stacked neatly. Get out!'

I see. No 'Oh my darling, how are you?' No tender gathering into the arms or feeling for broken bones. I was so hurt I didn't even think to fake it. Anyway I was just glad to get out. It was such a mess in there.

It took ages to get all those cobwebs off, but as a little revenge I left them all under Jenny's bed, on the novel she would be fishing for at bedtime. I was quite happy there and would have gone to sleep if it weren't for a recurrence of that horrible smell that had toppled me from my elevated position in the first place. I turned my head to the source. Jenny's legs were visible at the far end of the bed; she was wearing those old trainers she hadn't been able to find since we moved here. They were a bit mouldy and worn but she didn't seem to notice. They stank to high heaven!

I followed them out into the garden and watched as they attracted the puppies who immediately tried to chew and tear at the shoes. They didn't want that smell in the house again.

'Get off you little devils!' she said.

We had to put up with it all day until Ross came in. He'd sort it out.

He didn't, it got worse! She produced from the same box and with the same smell his sheepskin slippers which he had been missing terribly as they had holes cut out for his corns and hardly any chew marks.

He was delighted and sat wearing them all night on the settee. We all sat anywhere but the lounge.

That is the last time I go pottering.

Chocolate Round
the Chops

28–30 March

The other cats, the puppies and me didn't know what Easter was. All we heard was, 'You lot had better not steal my eggs at Easter!'; this from Jenny who is usually calling, 'No eggs for me,' or 'It doesn't have any egg in it does it?' whenever Ross cooks breakfast or dinner.

Bramble and Willow miaowed, 'As if we would.' And

Clover and Bracken just flopped those labrador ears around in a dopey, obedient way. The kittens were too busy duffing each other up to care.

But I am the clever one; I knew there must be something special about Easter eggs.

There was a smell of hot cross buns around the house all Friday. Big trays came out of the Aga loaded with fat, spicy cakes. When I got a chance to jump up on to the bench to look my stomach flipped. The buns had dead flies stuck all over them; no wonder they were cross.

Early on Sunday Jenny took the dogs out to the old sheds and stables. I thought she must have got some hens and gone egg collecting so I sneaked along behind them.

No hens! Just buckets, old rubbish and a big stick which Jenny would use to fight marauding brambles. They disappeared on a long walk across the fields and back; puppies panting, bottoms bouncing and sticky undergrowth clinging to everyone's legs.

How boring. I'd had a good all-over lick, a few swipes at bees who came to see who was sitting on the stable wall, and an hour's snooze. After the usual clattering about Jenny came over to the wall, ruffled my newly licked hairdo and said, 'Right, I'm off for my eggs.'

I could hardly keep up with those wellington boots until they came off at the door. The rest of her clothes dropped to the floor on her way to the shower. Ross was reading the papers in bed but he got out and stretched to feel around the top of the pine wardrobe from where he brought a big rustling bag.

'Ah-ha!' cried Jenny covered in towels. 'I knew you wouldn't forget.' She reached beneath the bed to produce a big box with a yellow bow right across. They both opened their presents to reveal huge foil-covered eggs. What a waste of a morning! Who would want to pinch Easter eggs anyway, so garish and boring. I jumped up on to the duvet and went to sleep.

I was woken by a smell. A sweet creamy smell that had drips falling from my chin.

Ross and Jenny were lying back in a fit-to-burst sleep with newspapers and wrapping paper everywhere. I tiptoed in towards the smell. There it was, acres of broken chocolate.

I licked and chewed until I almost burst. Slumping down between them it was hard to tell who was who, we were all so fat and sick with chocolate round the chops. Burp! (Pardon.)

Next Easter . . . forget it. I'm sleeping right through.

When we woke we were all feeling sick. Jenny cleared up the litter from all that chocolate and said she felt guilty. She started to tell Ross how she hated commercialism.

'Easter is about Jesus and bunnies and flowers,' Jenny said, measuring her hips. She didn't mention her diet.

She made all us cats and puppies go into the garden; it was sunny and we were told to enjoy spring as she had to plant things.

How come she can dig little holes in the borders when I am chased for it?

It was so boring and she worked way past lunch time. I got interested when she started to talk about food, only I couldn't see any. I would even have had a go at chocolate again.

'See this hedge Bluebell, it is full of Bread and Cheese.'

It looked like Hawthorn to me and was so full of prickles it wouldn't be going anywhere near my mouth.

'Isn't it lovely the way flowers have such appetising country names?' she droned on. 'Poached-egg flowers are so lovely in the sun,' she smiled. I love eggs so I made my legs fly down the path but there were only the usual leaves and flowers. My tummy rumbled on but Jenny showed no sign of going in.

'See Bluebell, in my herb garden there is a Curry plant.' No thank you. Did she think I would be interested in that?

In the borders she was spouting about Pineapple flower, Lollipop plant and Chocolate cosmos (yes please). She had me worn out, all that sniffing. I got most excited at Beefsteak plant, Buttercup, Cherry Pie and Strawberry and Cream. She said they were all plants but I worry about her. There wasn't a thing to be gobbled in the whole garden.

Then, just as she recognised her 'little darlin's' were all fainting with hunger, she dashed to that little round garden she tends in the middle of the lawn.

I was off, she might be about to discover what I leave there every night.

'These plants are especially for you pussy cats,' she said bending down. At last I thought we were going to have our rumbling tummies silenced, but no.

She showed us Mouse plant (no tail nor fur), Catmint (no whiskers), Fishtail fern (no water nor fins) and Snap-dragons (no fiery breath).

Was this all meant to frighten us? I just think she's mad.

When we finally got a nibble of lunch I bolted it and had a sore tum for the second time this Easter.

'Don't worry Bluebell,' she laughed with a sly look on her face. 'I've got something in the lounge that will make you feel better.'

This sounded like a treat but I no longer trusted her after this morning.

'Here, have as much as you like.' She pushed a shiny green leaf beneath my nose.

'Don't you know what it is Bluebell? It's a Caster-oil plant.'

She only laughed when I turned green.

April Fool

... ..

1 April

Jenny's face had reached 9½ on the 'up to something' scale.
    She said it was April Fool's day. She doesn't need one
special day for being foolish. She does quite well spreading
it out through the whole year but today I knew everyone
was in for it. Today she could get away with anything simply
by uttering that one worn-out phrase: 'April Fool!'

First thing this morning was when I felt the lash of her
wickedness. I had been flat out on her chest fast asleep and
expecting to stay that way for another half hour. Suddenly
she got up. I was surprised but started thinking 'Breakfast!'
I ran to the door to await the slippers and dressing-gown
routine but she didn't even leave the bed.

She giggled after that and lay down again, stabbed at the
TV remote control and looked extra comfy. I had started to
salivate and adrenalin sloshed through my veins to get me
ready for the race to the food bowls. I needed neither.

The rat.

When she did get up, she tipped cornflakes into our
dishes and went into the kitchen whistling. We sniffed and
looked at each other, was there a new food we hadn't heard
about? Willow and Bramble took a cornflake between their
teeth just in case but they couldn't eat it. It just stuck to
their lips and made them look ridiculous. The kittens scattered them everywhere, so that every step we took they
crunched into our toes.

Jenny peeped around the door. 'April Fool!' She laughed
and kept on laughing as she made Ross's coffee. Now he

needs that coffee to enter the world of the living again from wherever it is he goes where it is compulsory to snore and grunt all night. Her face was growing wilder and the tray shook as she carried it upstairs. I wasn't getting any breakfast so I followed her. The clock hadn't set off its alarm yet, so she fiddled with it until it did. He shuffled up and Jenny arranged the pillows behind his head. That was funny. It wasn't even his birthday. I jumped on to his lap and the sight was horrible. Puffy skin showed no hope of eyes or a mouth, and his hair looked like someone had given him a bouffant then karate-chopped it.

Jenny went into the shower room and I heard the water start. I also heard the door creep open just a bit, enough for someone to peep through. I moved down to sit on his toes then, I didn't want to be too close.

He managed, with shaking hands, to get the coffee mug to his mouth where he sipped. His usual 'Ahhh, that's lovely' started but stopped at the 'Ahhhh', which became louder and more grotesque the further his tongue stuck out.

'April Fool!' Jenny shouted from her secret viewing place.

'You've put salt in my coffee!' he bellowed like a wounded soldier.

'I know! Isn't it great to get away with it!'

He was too busy washing his mouth out to do anything back to her and later, just in case, she was extra nice to him. When she kissed him goodbye, it seemed to take much longer than usual which made me suspicious. I had no way of telling him as he bent to pick up his briefcase that he had a trail of red lipstick kisses around his clean white collar and up his cheek. It had grown quite pale as she'd reached his mouth and I glanced at Jenny; her mouth was now quite bare. He didn't have a clue.

She fed us then but we were suspicious and sniffed a lot before we ate: pity the puppies didn't do the same before they gobbled up the bone-biscuits she merrily tossed to them. They were covered in sticky treacle.

I stayed away from Jenny as much as I could but she gave me lunch and ruffled the hair I'd spent all morning flattening.

'Don't worry Bluebell. April Fool ends at midday. It's over. Wasn't it great!'

I didn't think so.

When I came in from flattening her daffodils I saw an apple pie cooling on the utility room bench. It was out of reach of the dogs but not the cats. She didn't think this mattered as we don't like apples.

This however made me think of something Jenny didn't like. I sniffed out Bramble and Willow and got them to help me with my plan. They were more than happy unlike the kittens who were still young enough to think everything Jenny did was OK by them.

Jenny put on lipstick and perfume to drink a glass of wine. That meant someone was coming and I was even more excited. I didn't care if it was after the cut-off time for April Fool.

Ross came home sooner than usual wearing a new shirt

I'd never seen before. He came in the back way and bent to put his lipsticked shirt in the washing machine. Then he noticed me and I thought all was lost.

Not so. As it happens I couldn't have done it without him.

I had got the five sacrificed mice on to the bench and had even picked the top crust off the pie to separate it from the bottom. I was having difficulty scooping out the apple to make way for the new filling. Also my helpers had disappeared. The puppies, after licking the first paw-scoop of zingy apple from the floor refused to help any more, thinking the pay not up to the job; anyway they had abandoned the plan in favour of bouncing 'hello' all over Ross.

He worked out very quickly that this was revenge pie ... best eaten cold he said, which was great as I had no idea what temperature mice would cook at.

He winced as he picked up the mice but smiled as he

pushed them into the centre of the pie then covered them up with apple, a touch I hadn't thought of.

He went off then to find Jenny who was in the lounge chatting to the new neighbours who talked very posh and seemed to have made Jenny do the same. I had to wait for ages.

All through avocado prawns my heart was beating in anticipation and I thought my chest would cave in while they all lingered over chicken-á-la-something out of a packet.

Ross kindly left the dining-room door open when he came out for the cream to go with the surprise pie and I went in. I thought of sneaking under the table but then I would only hear the excitement, which would have wasted all those divine expressions I hoped for. I made for the big display of dried flowers beside the dresser and hid there. I could see without being seen.

Ross cut the pie and smothered all three portions with cream as he passed them around. He said he was full and gave me a wink. Jenny put her spoon in the dessert and was the first to realise something was wrong.

Know what she did?

Nothing. She must have thought that only one mouse had got in there by accident and she would keep quiet and eat around it.

Her thoughts were forced to change as did the colours of her guests' faces: as spoons cut through pastry to reveal furry apples, they stopped.

They were furious and said they'd never been so insulted.

Jenny gave a sickly laugh and said a squeaky 'April Fool!'

It didn't have quite the same ring as it had that morning. She was suddenly on her own as Ross showed the ashen visitors where to find their coats. I wondered if I'd gone too far when I saw how upset she was, but my tenderness changed back to glee when Ross came back to have all three creamy plates of mouse pie thrown at him.

I don't think we have to worry about April the First next year.

Surprises Sprung

2–3 April

Spring again!? Jenny is out there leaping and throwing her arms around as if it was going to last.

April in England is not to be trusted. If she thinks a couple of sunbeams on her face and six deep breaths mean spring, then she doesn't know her slimy slugs from her wiggly worms.

She only has to watch us. None of our fur has started to fall out yet. Two ways I know this. One, when I lick I don't suddenly gain an unfeminine moustache, and two, the carpet hasn't yet become thicker and to my mind cosier.

The puppies make the greatest contribution. Though a black labrador, Clover can never out-shed the sheer volume that the golden retriever Bracken can.

It is the first spring we have had the kittens, but the sleek stripes of their fur don't look as if they'll offer much help to get the floor knee-deep before the inevitable cold day when Jenny will notice the thicker pile.

You see, as soon as the sap rises in the garden it seems to do the same in Jenny. One little twitter from a bird and frost that melts before nine and whoosh, she's out. Tools clatter from the shed, spiders are tipped from boots and every plant in the garden knows it has to put on a brave leaf and perform.

Only she's too soon!

Now Willow is blonde and her hair falls out constantly. She is a dreadful mess. It is nothing to do with her age, she has always been like that. Flowing locks stop flowing to show pink skin in fascinating little patches. What a sight. Jenny says she could have knitted a whole wardrobe of clothes with the amount of hair Willow leaves on the sofa. Only not in spring because Jenny doesn't notice, she's too busy snipping and feeding, digging and ignoring cups of tea Ross constantly leaves on garden walls.

She is always watching TV for weather forecasts, and tapping the barometer seems to be more important than combing her hair in the mornings: she could save all this time by just watching our furry little bodies.

No chance.

We are not included in her little dream of dickie-birds and English country gardens. Whole cans of cat food are slopped into dishes and biscuits tipped in a mountain that spills to the water-sloshed floor when she slams the kitchen door. She doesn't notice anything that doesn't have roots or feathers. As far as she's concerned winter is over, so it's outside or nowhere.

We have a great time. This is when we can do anything we want and get away with it. Whilst her eyes and hands are out there, so is her mind. She doesn't look at any housework until the wind changes and the rain makes puddles where she last made footprints.

The garden is so different with Jenny in it. Usually it is full of mystery. Little rustles set my imagination going. At first I think it is the wind, then a vulnerable little mouse. That's when I get interested. I crouch and search; as my keenness grows, so do my thoughts. It could be a badger . . . or a fox . . . or a lion!

That's when I rattle the cat-flap at a million miles an hour and everyone thinks the devil is after me. I've never stayed around long enough to find out.

No, when Jenny comes out everything is reduced to that base human level. She spoils it all. Mole hills are flattened, vole holes are caved in and undergrowth we've hidden in all winter is torn from the ground. The garden looks as if a nuclear war has been its inspiration.

But you know, she gets it right. Soon it will be abundant and voluptuous with smells you wouldn't believe.

I have tried to save her from pain by rubbing against her legs to show her how fluffy I am in my winter coat but it doesn't work. She can't feel anything through mud-caked wellies. Anyway she is too carried away by the leaping Lupins and burgeoning Begonias of her imagination to notice. And I don't like the speed with which that four-pronged fork attacks the ground. So I leave her to it and come in to polish off that half-eaten chicken sandwich she's left on the table. I have to make muddy paw-prints all over the gardening book left open beside it.

Uh-oh!

Here comes the rain. It is cold enough to turn to snow. She'll be in in a minute. Mumbling and complaining.

'If it gets frosty, I'll lose all my seedlings and shoots!'

She'll run a hot bath and moan and groan about her back.

I wonder how long she'll take to notice there is no fur on the carpets yet. It is all still on her 'little darlin's' backs and bottoms.

That's the door slamming. Her coat is wet and her socks are wet. But wettest of all is her face.

Told you it would end in tears.

But not for me. I've got a new place to sleep. Jenny says I'll have to get off . . . but I won't. She has hurt her back after all that gardening and has to lie flat on the floor. She is hot, weak and powerless.

The new place is her tummy. It is the squidgiest cushion I have ever had and even comes with its own musical rumblings.

I first found out how comfy a tummy can be when I saw Jenny crawl in from the garden. She dragged herself past the food dishes moaning and groaning all the way. I followed her into the sitting room where she went over the top with 'AAAHs' and 'OW! OW! OWs!' as she gingerly lay down on the carpet. Who was she trying to impress? Only her little darlin's were around. We've seen it all before. Bracken and Clover rushed over thinking she was playing puppy games. Their frolicking and nudging seemed to make things worse and the kittens ran to hide.

Gosh, she was noisy! I thought of lying over her mouth but the mood she was in she'd have bitten me. Willow and Bramble, being sensitive cats, sniffed and licked anything pink but by now this didn't include Jenny's face which was purplish-red.

'AHHHH! Bluebell, I'm in agony and it's hours till Ross gets home!'

That's when I got the idea and climbed aboard. She couldn't get her arms far enough up to knock me off so I settled down to a nice comfy afternoon.

I was woken by my bed jiggling. There were gentle whines and sobbings which seemed to be triggered off by Ross's key in the door. The waterworks were for his sympathy which he gave in buckets. He slobbered and rubbed all over her while she whispered the tale of too much weeding. I was right up to her face and boy did she make the best of it!

'Get off Bluebell,' he said, quite aggressively I thought to someone who had been guarding his wife for hours.

I wouldn't move so he lifted me off. My paws thudded on to the carpet. He went off to the kitchen. I got straight back on my new bed which by now was shuddering gently. So relaxing!

He came back with a duvet and Jenny's medicine which is called 'a cup of tea'.

'Oh, darling,' she whimpered. A bit over the top I thought, as she'd given him an earful before he'd left for work. 'I have a cat's-eye view of you standing over me. You look just like a pylon in Levis!'

I'd known that for years just like I knew a cat's-eye view of Jenny was a scarecrow in a tent.

They laughed, and she even said that hurt too.

I've been on the tummy for three weeks now with little breaks for nature, and sometimes my place is taken by a book. Jenny is moving about quite a bit when we are alone, but as soon as Ross appears she's flat out moaning and groaning again. It must have something to do with all that housework and cooking he is doing.

She is limp and shapeless just like a slug on a rug.

If she throws me off her tummy once more I will tell Ross the truth! But he'll know soon enough when he looks in the biscuit tin and finds all the chocolate ones gone.

Bird Bombed

12–13 April

Jenny has given me a special place to catch birds. It's a tiny box with an even tinier hole; I don't know how she expects me to get my big paws in there! You'd think she'd have given it a bit more thought. Also she has had Ross nail it to a tree, almost at the top for heaven's sake. I know I'm fat and need exercise but this is stretching both comfort and my furry little legs just too far.

I have never actually caught a bird. They all know that I am not allowed, but sometimes I make a show. I jump into the air too late and so they peck up crumbs right in front of my nose. A bunch of blue-tits mobbed me once. They pulled tufts of my lovely fur clean out and flew up to line their nests with it. Just think of all those babies snuggling up each night in my well-groomed coat whilst I walked around with bald patches!

That's why I thought it was fair when Jenny brought the tit box, to even up the score a little. She caught me sniffing at it and scowled 'Don't you dare!' She asked Ross if she should put some bedding in for the tits. I thought she was joking, and when he replied, 'Oh no, only some towels and soap,' I knew she was serious. I had wondered how birds stay so clean without a long, rough tongue like mine.

I wondered if birds had food dishes in there: they'd have to be awfully small, but I heard they eat caterpillars and

seeds. I can't believe that! The food would crawl off or grow into petunias if they were late home for supper.

I had a peep into a nest the other day.

At first I saw little blue eggs snuggling in a lot of feathers. They were far too small for Ross to fit his buttered soldiers into, so I didn't think I should show Jenny. Next morning I took Willow up as she wouldn't believe me. She said eggs came from the supermarket in cardboard boxes.

I had to manoeuvre my fat little bottom carefully and space was tight. We couldn't both look at the same time.

'See!' Willow triumphed. 'No eggs!'

She slid down and stamped off not wanting to associate with a liar.

I swung up the ivy for a better look, wondering if I had climbed the wrong tree as I peeped again over the moss nest.

She was right: there were no eggs, just five little prehistoric pink wriggly things with bulging eyes that didn't open and enormous mouths that certainly did. They had a few grey feathers stuck higgledy-piggledy into see-through skin. They were trying to camouflage themselves as birds so they wouldn't be blamed for eating those eggs I saw yesterday.

The shock of all this had me on the ground again in seconds. I wouldn't let Jenny know we had such weird creatures in our garden. She'd want to move again. I kept quiet. I have to protect the weak.

Secretly, I like the birds. Apart from pinching the top off my milk on winter mornings, they give me hours of fun as I watch them on the bird table.

Jenny never forgets to put lots of food out for them during the winter, otherwise I wouldn't have any fledglings in my box. Don't worry, I won't be climbing that tree again. I've had enough of monsters anyway, I might get mugged and my fur has only just grown back from last year.

Pressing Problem

8 May

Jenny says she is changing my name – to GOBBLE!
What a name! What a cheek!

I don't know where she got the idea from. As if I'm greedy. Everyone likes to eat don't they? I'm not the only one. She can talk, have you seen the size of her thighs in those leggings? I think she keeps her lunch in there . . . and her spare cardigan.

I know it all started the day I got stuck in the cat-flap. I had been hoping she hadn't noticed that my tummy fitted the hole exactly. It'd been a bit of a struggle for a few days but that day I stuck. It must have been extra fur because I can't remember having too much breakfast, although Willow was out doping around as usual so I probably ate hers as well.

I heard those shoes that Jenny wears only when she's out lunching click across the tiles and then felt a little shove on my bottom.

'Need some help, Bluebell?'

I looked around nonchalantly as if I was admiring the view but she wasn't fooled.

'There is a queue behind you Bluebell.' I didn't believe her but I wouldn't put it past those slim little kittens to want to get out at such an inconvenient time.

I wiggled my front legs and then I tried to get purchase with my back legs but it didn't work, none of my paws touched the ground but all of my tummy touched the cat-flap.

'I've been warning you this would happen Bluebell. It's a diet for you, now!'

I had to admit that I would have to cut down a bit, and as soon as she got me out of here, I'd give her a face rub to show I'd oblige. Only she didn't get me out, she started to walk away. I miaowed most pitifully. That brought her back.

'What?'

'Get me out!'

'No! You have to learn not to be so greedy Bluebell, and I said you are going on a diet now and that is what I meant: NOW! I know you are safe from any food or wildlife whilst your head is in the garden and your bottom is in the kitchen. As far as your tummy is concerned, it's "No pain, no wane."'

She walked away again and stayed away.

It was starting to rain. My front was gleaming with little raindrops and getting wetter by the second, my back was in the dry, centrally-heated house. I felt the plastic flap blowing in the wind and bashing me every now and again on that thin bit of skin where a cat's spine is most on show.

What was I to do?

I remembered why I wanted to go out in the first place and that was becoming more urgent. This was weally weird with a capital 'WEE!'

I tried to admire the view but black plastic dustbins and a makeshift step made from a pile of bricks didn't hold much fascination right at that moment.

The puppies bounded up from the top of the garden and licked my face. I could do nothing to stop them, no biffs or bashes from flaying paws, no quick get-aways. All I could do was scrunch up my face and promise to get even when I got out. That would be when I got slim, which could be a long time. They knew it.

As if I wasn't suffering enough indignity, I began to be aware of a cold nose on my bottom, then another. Perhaps the kittens thought the shock might dislodge me, perhaps they were just taking advantage. I was past caring. I'd be here for weeks . . . months even. I would spend my time being swung in and out of the house as they all used the door as normal. I'd have to have my Christmas lunch in this undignified position. Jenny would put a paper hat on me and put my bowl

just out of reach. Then I remembered dinners were the last thing I'd get here, which didn't cheer me up.

So that's it then! Christmas will be just a blow in the face with a rolled up party whistle and a smack on the bum with a cracker. Wonderful!

Perhaps I'd shrink from the cold. But that wouldn't work either as only my front bit would diminish and that bit was already out. I couldn't go backwards as the flap would rattle along my spine like a xylophone.

Something distracted the puppies who ran away around the side of the house and then skipped back with Jenny. She had a wood-saw and a pack of butter. I nearly fainted.

She laughed. 'Just kidding Bluebell! Learnt your lesson yet? Going to give up Gobbling for Britain?'

I sniffed with what I hoped was the most pitiful sniff of my life, and it worked. She put the saw on the garden wall and took a handful of butter. Tucking and shoving seemed to be her hidden talent and I wanted to giggle when she worked at the bit of my tummy which was now quite sore as it was squeezed and gripped by the flap. Nothing happened except that the puppies ran away with the rest of the butter.

She left me dangling there, my hair a greasy mess, my face wet with rain and slobber and my spirits as deflated as I wish my tummy could have been. I felt butter-slicked hands prodding me from behind and then she sort of twisted me at the same time as her knee pushed me, rather harder than necessary I thought.

I came out with a sort of plop. A pile of buttered grey fur on the gravel.

Jenny opened the door and laughed. 'It's a bath for you Bluebell, and then we'll discuss that diet you need to go on. I see the vet has some very appetising bags of dried food especially for cats who like to guzzle too much.'

I would have liked a cuddle and a good rub on that sore bit but the thought of eating cardboard gave me the strength to run.

After all, shampoo and warm water wouldn't be half as good as a rough tongue at removing so much butter.

And not half so fattening!

Eye Opener

17 May

They've had a fight. It was great!

Ross dared to throw some waste food into the bin. He knew Jenny had broken it into little pieces for the bird table. She read somewhere that if you give a third of your food to the birds you'll go to Heaven. She has no chance! The way she shrieks when I just saunter along the work tops or lick the meat.

The puppies were all for Ross; they think all leftovers should be for them but they were confused as he often calls them dustbins. We cats, who don't like boiled potatoes and crusts anyway, didn't take sides. We aren't even allowed to look at birds, never mind chase them, so why should they have any of our food.

I get away with anything when they are shouting at each other as they are too busy looking for things to throw to notice me.

I bit the tops off two plants and then sicked them up again into Jenny's leather boots, drank some of that beer stuff Ross has every night (don't do it, it's horrible), and then swung on the wires dangling from the back of the TV.

As the soap theme tune cut off, so the loud voices of Ross and Jenny cut in. They ganged up on me with a loud, 'Bluebell!!! You've broken the TV!'

I was off through the cat-flap but they opened the door and followed me. Up the brick path, through the rickety old gate and into the orchard.

I was at top speed, my hair streaking back when I heard a thump and then a loud crack.

Everything stopped except me. I had such a speed up that I just kept going. I turned my head to see what had happened and BANG, I crashed into the widest apple tree.

I could see stars and a part of my tummy I'd never seen before.

'Oh you poor little girl,' I could hear Ross call softly.

I lay still trying to look as sad as possible, but no loving hand came to smooth my ruffled hair. It was getting uncomfortable in this position, so I just peeped to see how far away he was. There was no one to be seen. I wriggled up and limped to the gate and there was Ross helping Jenny into the house.

I followed, feeling very neglected.

'I hope it's not broken,' Ross said, gently moving Jenny's arm. He was kissing and cuddling her like she was as adorable as me and she had a tear down her cheek. False, I bet!

I jumped on to her knee and she smiled.

'Oh Bluebell, we are all naughty aren't we? Life is too short to be cross.' Well I know who is the naughtiest in this house and it isn't me. (Oh, all right, it is.)

But I'm not as daft as humans, never could be. The things Jenny does never cease to amaze me. Ross has been extra nice after last night; she had her breakfast in bed, lay around reading the paper and then had a shower . . . at 10 a.m.!

She was slow getting dressed, and when she sat at her dressing table with all those bottles, I knew we'd be there for ages.

The phone rang when Jenny had put make-up on only one eye.

She dropped me from her lap, tucked the receiver between her ear and shoulder and went walk-about. She slopped from the bedroom to the kitchen and put water in the kettle, boiled it and sat down with a cup of tea. Never stopped talking once!

I jumped up in front of her. She looked stupid. One eye was wide, rimmed in black and dark curly lashes; the other one seemed to belong to an albino pig. Or Jenny on New Year's morning.

I had heard that blondes have more fun. Well if this is how they get their laughs they can keep blonde.

I am happy with my grey colour although Ross seems to hate his every grey hair that turns up suddenly. He pulls and plucks until he is sure it's all gone. He should get the mirror around the back, that would give him something to really pluck at.

Why do people have to be painting their faces, screwing up their hair and squirting stinky stuff under their arms? What for? They can never look nice. Jenny says it helps in her war with nature. This is from the same mouth that shouts at Ross if he pulls cow parsley from the borders, stamps on a ladybird or walks too near a bird when it is nesting! Whose side is she on then?

I watched that mouth as it slurped tea and talked incessantly. It was pale and wrinkly. I knew as soon as she could find her way upstairs again it would be red, smooth and much bigger than nature had given her. She seems to have lost that particular fight.

I grew bored then, licked the chocolate off two biscuits and went to sleep on a magazine on the table ... right in front of her and she didn't even notice. That is what gossip is for, keeping you tied up so cats can do what they like.

That horrible doorbell rocketed sweet dreams from me and the phone from Jenny, although I notice she didn't put it back where it belonged to recharge what must be very flat batteries.

At the door was a very attractive man. I knew this by the way Jenny said, 'Oh hhh! Hello, how may I help?' She used a sickly sweet voice and fluffed her hair up with girly fingers. He was at the wrong house and Jenny giggled as she pointed to next door.

He left but she didn't shut the door until he was completely out of view. Usually unexpected callers almost lose their noses.

She picked the phone up again and said, 'Oh Margaret, you should have seen who it was! What a hunk. Gorgeous blue eyes and those shoulders! He seemed to like me too, you should have seen his pupils widen and he couldn't stop smiling.'

I bet he couldn't! She had obviously forgotten what she was doing when the phone interrupted. I hung around until she went back upstairs and looked in the mirror. It would make my day. The scream would only last for seconds but the embarrassment for weeks.

'Aiyyeeee! I'm going to kill myself!'

I hoped she didn't. It was almost time for my lunch.

The New
Trousers

6–7 June

Ross has some new trousers.

I don't like them! Oh, they are fashionable enough in the got-to-look-younger, got-to-look-fit way that he seems to have made his own lately, but they don't suit everyone.

Us cats, for instance. We aren't allowed any pleasure from anything new that comes into this house. It becomes a nightmare of 'get off's and 'don't-you-dare's.

Well the new trousers are no different.

I didn't even notice his legs were clad in the latest fashion. The only point my eyes picked up on, in mid-spring between the carpet and his lap, was the surprisingly hair-free glow that covered where I was heading.

I must have landed, I always do, but I was back on the carpet before any sense of touch had reached my paw-pads never mind my brain.

From there I observed frenzied hand brushing and rubbing. Ross was determined to rid his new trousers of any trace of me and most of the top nap too. These were cosy trousers, I could see that now I knew there was something to study. They were thick and floppy and only gave a rough hint that this shape was to cover legs. A neat bow was formed from the drawstring pulled tighter than necessary around his waist.

These were sports trousers. The sort sweating squash

players pull carelessly over tiny shorts when they've finished sweating. I know because I've seen them on TV when
Jenny watches it to admire the players' bottoms. She hates
sport. So does Ross. So why did he have this particular type
of new trousers and why was he sitting on the settee watching soaps with a box of toffee on his lap? They were for
jumping around in not slopping around in.

Jenny came in then with a big plate of chips.

'Oh, you got them then,' she said plonking down next
to him. 'Comfy?'

'Yup.'

'Cosy?'

'Yup.'

'Costly?'

'Yup.'

She got him! And he knew it. She'd be off to spend the

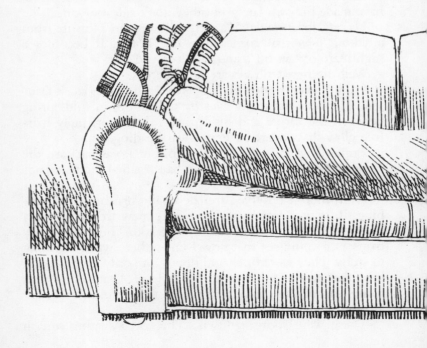

78

same amount of money on herself tomorrow. He couldn't complain.

He slid over the shock of being caught and went back to his toffee, only this time it was alternated with chips.

When the soap finished he got up and spun around in true modelling style to solicit Jenny's response.

If she was staring at me so she wouldn't laugh, it didn't work. I thought he looked hilarious too.

'Too fat,' she said with all the economy of a true couch and telly addict.

He looked offended, pinched a handful of chips from Jenny's plate and left.

'His gym course starts tomorrow Bluebell.' She smiled, patting her knee with such welcome grace. I was on there like a flash, under the chip plate but in that lovely little hammock her skirt makes.

Next night Ross came home sweating but with no 'nice little-bottom shorts' on display. Jenny wouldn't have looked anyway, she's seen it all before. His new trousers had bagged at the knee and his body had bagged at the middle bit, just where he likes to bend to the fridge for a beer.

Jenny laughed and the puppies threw themselves on the new trousers in a frenzy of hairy home-welcoming. Ross didn't utter a word of warning. No pride for his clothing was capable of coming from his broken body. But his lips seemed only just capable of wrapping themselves around a beer bottle.

Willow woke in her picnic hamper from where she surveys the world and Bramble ambled in through the cat-flap with a mouse for a moustache.

We all followed Ross into the sitting room where he collapsed full length on to a sofa.

We waited until the 'OHHHs' and 'AHHHs' finished and then we pounced. All of us at once!

He was covered in cats and dogs. The new trousers were nowhere to be seen. Lost in fur, mud and those little unknown bits that seem to fall from animals whenever they snuggle up.

He never peeped protest. Even when Bramble ate the mouse on a particularly tender bit of his anatomy.

The Entertainer

9 June

Are fur balls offensive?
No, they are not.

Ugly maybe and sometimes inconvenient. But never offensive.

How can something so natural be offensive?

How can anything to do with nice little pussycats be anything but wonderful?

This morning Ross was enjoying the early June sunshine with a mug of coffee and a slice of toast slapped with marmalade. He wandered out into the garden to see if the roses were budding and free himself from the responsibility of crumbs and cup rings.

He was just about to take an enormous bite when I felt that old familiar heave. It started with a tickle in my throat which was quickly backed up with a muscle spasm in my tummy. Out it came at his feet, long slimy and packed with fur. It had a few wet biscuits at the front and was guarded at the rear with a bit of mouse tail.

I studied it with interest, then I studied Ross with greater interest.

He was standing open-mouthed with toast wavering round, he had gone pale and looked ever so weak. The toast seemed to toss itself into the hedge just before the coffee poured itself on to the flowerbed.

He moved very slowly indoors and through the open window I could hear words like 'revolting and disgusting'.

What was he talking about? I ran in to see.

81

'OK Bluebell? Feel better for that?' Jenny said smiling.

'Oh yes, ask her how she is! Not a care for my feelings. Why don't you think about me first instead of animals?' exclaimed Ross.

'I do think of you darling. I think that if this is the first fur ball you have ever seen then you have lived a charmed life. Show me where it is then.' He had a second near-faint then and really went to town on his feelings.

'Do you really expect me to go back out there? Where that thing is! It is so offensive I shall never eat again.' That turned out to be a lie because when Jenny went out to have a look and then went back in for clearing-up stuff he was already pouring milk on to cornflakes.

She sauntered on to the lawn and was distracted by a wren in the hedge. It was chirping loudly and Jenny thought it might be warning her to keep away from where it was

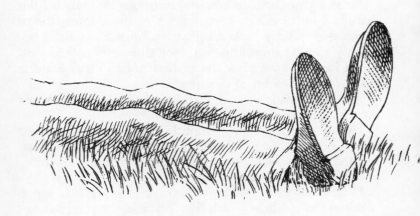

building a nest. She kept very still so as not to frighten it. Jenny loves wrens, says she is called after one. Who ever heard of a bird called Jenny Wren? She makes things up!

Anyway, that delayed her removal of my fur ball. When we got back to it there were flies everywhere. Jenny poked at the fur ball to check what was in it as she wants to keep an eye on my health. She used an old fork from the pet-feeding cupboard.

Ross, thinking the coast was clear and that the world's most frightening object had been dealt with, came out to say goodbye for the day.

He just caught her forking at the hairy bit. He really fainted then. I have never seen so many petals flattened in one go. Jenny was more mad about that than the fact she was married to a wimp.

She left him where he fell and tossed the fur ball into

the hedge to join the wasp-covered toast and several other day-to-day bits that would have Ross in a coma (if he knew).

I licked Ross's face, there was milk around his mouth.

He was coming round and Jenny helped him to his feet. I thought she would tell him he had torn his shirt or at least that he had coffee-mud on his bottom, but no! She said just one word.

'MEN!'

I have never seen such a fuss in all my life. He went off to work looking a complete shambles and mumbling about the joys of having animals. The puppies came back from their romp in the paddock, drank a bowl of water and then joined Bramble and Willow in the search for the sunniest patches.

Jenny took me inside and pulled slices of chicken from the sandwiches Ross had forgotten to take to work.

'Here you are Boobies. Have to fill that stomach up. You mustn't have got much past that blockage for a few days.'

It was lovely. I had had a good heave, a good laugh and now good food.

Fur balls are not offensive and they are not round either. But they can be very entertaining, don't you think?

Stringing me Along

☙

12–14 June

I'm being exploited!
There must be some Cat Line I can phone to make a complaint against Jenny. She says I am spoilt, given the best of everything. I might have agreed until I heard her on the phone thanking someone for a cheque for something I had done.

She never even let on. Made me think I was honoured to have lots of new toys to choose from. I came in from sitting on the bird table and found something new to sniff in the kitchen. It was a square of brown carpeted wood with a tube wound round and round with string. On the top of the tube was a ping-pong ball dangling on another bit of string.

'Go on Bluebell, have a go!'

I sat on the cold tiles and studied this wonder of modern manufacture.

What was it? Have a go? Have a go at what?

How did anyone have a go at carpet and string?

My eyes scanned the thing in front of them but were disadvantaged by the effort my brain had to put in to work out how to please this woman who was now promising me just-cooked minced beef if I co-operated.

I hit out with my paw and sent the ball into outer space, or rather it would have travelled that far had it not been restricted to six inches by the string.

Jenny wasn't pleased. 'Oh Bluebell, have a go! Go on!'

She sighed in a 'flaming-heck' kind of way, thumped down on the table with a note pad and pen she'd been holding and then lunged at me.

I hadn't time to be off, Jenny has lightning limbs when she has something important to do.

She grabbed my front paws (roughly I thought for someone trying to get a favour out of someone else) and rubbed them up and down on that spiral of string that a person must have spent hours winding so neatly round and round the tube.

'Get off!' I yowled.

I'd get my claws out if she did that again. I'd never used them on her but then I'd never been manhandled into being an idiot before either.

'Oh for heaven's sake Bluebell, get your claws out!'

What! I was shocked. She wanted me to slash her to ribbons with razor-decorated paws. I couldn't. It's not in my nature.

Besides I could smell that beef cooking.

She grabbed me then and bent down. My nose was a centimetre from that carefully applied string.

'Just scratch the wretched scratching post will you Bluebell! Just once so I can write a report.'

A post . . . just for scratching. What are trees for, and fences and other people's gate posts and garden table legs?

Why didn't she just ask, in a polite way?

Even though I'd just had a good old claw-heave on the old chestnut tree, I obliged with a little tickle.

You'd have thought I had just conquered the world, she was so pleased. She scribbled copious notes and polished my head with her hand.

It was nice to see her smiling at least, so I went towards the cooker and sniffed.

'Oh no Bluebell, not yet!'

She opened the kitchen door and there on the hall carpet was another weird contraption. I could see through to the lounge where there were three more so I ran up to Jenny's study where I don't get into trouble for jumping on the bed. I wasn't safe even there. Attached to the wall with screws was an expensive-looking piece of wood and string.

There was no escape: I knew I'd be denied peace, sleep or any kind of food until I had co-operated. That minced beef was wafting up my nostrils, persuading me to do things I didn't really want to.

Jenny had followed me and was glaring. I knew then that a cat has got to do what a cat has got to do.

I stretched and scratched on the up-market version and then went into the hall where I stretched and scratched. I did four stretch-and-scratches in the living room and then was faced with a surprise stretch-and-scratch in the dining room. If there were any more I'd have a change: scratch before I stretched. That'd have her pen scribbling.

Jenny seemed mildly satisfied and put some mince to cool for me. That's when Willow and Bramble came in through the flap and started bouncing around beneath the bench my mince was on.

Jenny seemed delighted, put two more dishes of meat to cool and grabbed her note pad.

I think it must have been my scent or the little bits of nail sheath I left dangling in the string but these two got the idea straight away. They jingled bells and tickled string, romping from room to room as if they were on holiday.

Jenny's wrist nearly snapped with the excitement of being able to report all this action.

Do you know, they had all disappeared the next morning. We were scratching post-less, except for the one in the study which Ross refused to remove, saying it would damage the wall.

I was happy for a while until we had a magazine through the door. Jenny pounced on *Your Cat* and turned quickly to a page she had her picture on. There, over two pages were photos of our scratching posts and reports of how we had liked them.

Well I'd liked the mince better but Willow and Bramble had been very enthusiastic.

That's when Jenny had thanked the editor for the cheque . . . for *our* work! What did we get? Some cheap old mince.

Well she won't get away with it again. Anything new appearing in this house and I'll get out my claws alright . . . to tear it to shreds. That'll give her plenty to write about!

Horrible Holiday

16–23 June

Jenny says holidays are refreshing, invigorating and that everyone should have one. Well I've had one and they're horrible.

I don't know why people rave about them or why they go away white and come back brown. It's also a puzzle to me where they buy those stuffed donkeys with Spanish hats or all those bottles of wine Ross calls El Plonko.

'We are all going away for our annual holiday,' Jenny had cooed as she dolloped chicken in jelly all over the work surface and up her arm. She passed me a bowl with the little offering that had actually hit its target. 'You, Bramble, Pussy Willow and the kittens are going to a different hotel to the puppies.' That didn't bother me, a whole fortnight of not being stood on, slobbered on or generally herded into little places their sniffling noses couldn't reach would be welcome.

Jenny packed all her new clothes in a big suitcase and Ross's old ones in a little one. Bracken and Clover had gone to 'Rover's Rave-Up' early that morning as they couldn't be trusted to stay clean all day. We cats sniffed all the swimming suits and sun lotions and then curled up on top of newly ironed T-shirts.

Three rude awakenings later we were stuffed into travelling baskets and lined up at the front door with battered luggage and a big straw hat I was pleased I'd never seen before.

'Passports! Pesetas! Just-in-case-jumper!' Jenny shrieked at Ross although I don't know why; he was standing right in front of her.

I still didn't know where we were off to but it sounded

sunny and I love sunny. I hadn't been to 'the airport' before but I was sure I'd like it as much as 'abroad' which was another place new to me.

We stopped the car on the way. I thought they'd got lost and they were calling at Pussy Paradise to ask the way. Jenny stayed in the passenger seat sobbing, 'I can't look! Just do it quickly.' Ross manhandled our baskets out of the car and the last I saw of Jenny she had her face in a hanky. I thought she liked holidays.

A lady who was trying to be nice took over and Ross and Jenny sped away. I called out, 'Hey! What about our holiday?' But it didn't come out right as I was being cuddled to within an inch of my life.

We were put in a pen with a new cushion and lots of newspapers. What a waste. I'm the only one who can read. I didn't know if this was abroad or the airport but I was starting to think it was neither. After we'd bounced our noses off everything new we settled down to supper and a good sleep but it didn't last long.

We had a wire run with a big log and two balls with tinkling little bells inside. From that direction we heard a big rattle and yowl. We dashed out to see a big ginger tom clinging to the other side of the wire shaking and scratting. 'Oh isn't he handsome,' sighed Bramble.

'Divine,' whined Willow. The kittens admired his muscles.

I thought he was rude and irritating so I gave him a punch in the mouth.

I got plenty of sleep as no one was speaking to me.

The rest of the holiday went downhill from there. I was bored, even with fresh newspapers every day. The others spent their time flirting or showing off. When the traitors returned, all smiles and hugs, I ignored them. It was easy, I had to prove a point. I only honoured them with a leg rub when I heard Ross say, 'Next year we'll get a house-sitter in and they won't even notice we are away.'

As if!

Maybe they won't even notice the little surprise I'm planning to leave in their suitcase either.

Horse Play

28 June

I've seen my first horse! Couldn't believe it.

That Jenny decided two dogs and five cats weren't enough. She wanted a hobby and so she was buying a horse. We cats didn't actually know what a horse was but we didn't let on. I just said, 'Oh how nice. Perhaps we can pinch its food and lie in its bed.' Willow and Bramble just licked their lips and nodded. They aren't as clever as me.

We heard Jenny on the phone, arranging to choose a horse on Saturday morning. Willow, Bramble and I got up early that morning and lined up on the garden wall, me in the best place of course. Nothing happened. We'd all licked ninety per cent of our bodies as we tried to look casual and disinterested before Jenny came out of the house. She drove off and returned fifteen minutes later with a carrying bag bearing the words 'Pick Your Own'.

I looked at Willow and she looked at Bramble. None of us knew why Jenny hadn't stopped to show us the new arrival. Was she worried we'd be jealous of this tiny new pet or that we'd not welcome it into our home?

Three rattles of the cat-flap later we were all up on the kitchen bench but there was no sign of the horse or the little carrying bag it came in. Jenny opened the door from the lounge and we knew we were for it by the look on her face.

'GET!' shove; 'OFF!' shove; 'THERE!' shove.

Three shocked pussies looked up from the floor. 'We know. We've been told a thousand times before! But where is it? The newest member of our family?' We gave our most beguiling of looks but it was no good. Jenny put the kettle to boil, rattled some tea cups and ignored us. Then she opened the fridge to get milk and horror of horrors; it was there, that carrying bag! In the fridge!

What sort of pet would want to live in a fridge? It's freezing in there. I know, I once got shut in when I pinched some cream. My fur stuck up on end and I was terrified of the dark. It was horrible.

When she put the milk away, she dipped her hand into the carrying bag and we all got excited. She was going to show us the horse. But she didn't. She just pinched its food. She popped a big red strawberry into her mouth and pushed the door shut with her bottom.

We were disgusted. This horse failed to interest us further and I made for the stairs hoping the bedroom door had been left open. Just as I leapt on to the duvet, the doorbell chimed.

'Oh she's adorable, divine, beautiful!'

Those words were usually only uttered in praise of me. What was going on? I ran down, flipped the flap and skidded across the gravel.

There was a monster in our yard. A dinosaur!

Jenny was kissing its big black neck and letting it lick her hand. YUK! Silently, I crept around. It had the biggest tail I have ever seen. It moved its feet and the noise was horrendous. It wore iron shoes that clattered to the ground scattering pebbles everywhere.

'I'll take her,' Jenny said. 'No need to bring any more. This is the horse for me.'

So this was a horse. I couldn't believe it. How could Jenny have a horse sitting on her knee in the evenings, how could it fit through the door let alone the flap? As a pet it was disastrous.

Jenny says she named her new pet Raven as it is black. But she hasn't been under its tummy like I have. There are all sorts of ginger bits there.

As for me sleeping in its bed, the horse has stolen one of mine, a favourite in the stable behind the house. And I won't be pinching its food either, have you seen what horses eat? It's disgusting!

Cross Look

4 July

I got such a fright!
   I was sitting at the end of the sofa on Jenny's knee being zozzled by Jenny rubbing the sticky-up bits of my ears between her fingers. She went dopey too, it was so relaxing.

That is when Farthing made a silent kitten-leap from where we couldn't see him up on to the arm of the sofa where we definitely could. His claws made such a ripping noise and he was so quick we both jumped sky high. I landed upside down on the floor (unknown for me) and Jenny was standing, only the cup of tea she had in her hand was still in sitting position . . . spilt!

Farthing was gone so quick that I wondered if it happened at all. Dandelion was under the coffee table and got the 'look' as he was the only kitten there. That's the trouble with having two kittens who look almost alike, but only for Jenny. They smell different so we little darlin's have no trouble distinguishing them.

I can tell where each of them has spent the night, who has eaten from which bowl and who has jumped on to the bench. Jenny can't, so nobody gets the blame.

'They're only little Bluebell. I daren't be unjust.'

Unjust! She didn't think of that when I was in trouble for ripping the stuffing out of a cushion. I got the blame because my distinctively coloured hairs were all over the ugly thing.

One sniff would have told her it was Clover. But I got

the finger wag and cross voice. That is bad enough but I went cuddle-less all day. I had to put on a really cute look before she would even ruffle my ears.

I hope there is some book somewhere which lists all the injustices towards me. Mind you, it would have just as many pages of things I got away with and laughed about, while another innocent darlin' got it in the neck.

They need to look out for themselves. It is tough around here.

Sometimes I think I'll be off to live in the wild. But Jenny says there are no biscuits or mince out there but there are combs and worm pills. That is what keeps me at home suffering, the thought of all those wild combs and worm pills dragging at your hair and pushing themselves down your throat!

Jenny is good at blaming Ross for everything she does. He is so amazed at the sheer diversity and cleverness of her accusations that he never argues. He says, 'Women are never to blame are they?' I know the truth; Jenny wants to appear perfect, so she works things backward in her brain to arrive at the reason that it is Ross's fault. It is brilliant really; she learned it from her mother and I learned it from her. Only I can't carry it out with such Oscar-winning performances. I always spoil it by peeping around the corner when I know I have laid a trail to blame someone else. What's the point of such efforts if you don't hang around for the show?

It is so easy to set the kittens up. They don't think things out, just barge into every situation. I never allow Willow to take the blame even when she is guilty. She is getting on a bit and anyway she is so giving. When I first arrived at the House Of Horrors, as I thought of Jenny and Ross's home, I had come straight from my mummy's, and those brothers and sisters who all looked like little balls of grey fluff, and Willow mothered me. She'd had her own blonde little babies and she recognised my distress.

She taught me that stairs weren't so high as they looked and beds really could be jumped on if you got the wiggle right, and she cuddled me.

How could I let her take any blame? My shoulders are broader than hers and I am far cheekier. I would give her anything (except minced steak which she eats far too slowly). Anyway, I am helping her by providing competition so that she eats more quickly.

Bramble is another story – she has a typical 'Don't think that just because I'm little' attitude. She is most adventurous and so loving with Jenny and Ross. She 'suckies' bits of their jumpers or towelling bath robes. They love it and have spent many an evening with a wet point on their left shoulder. If they saw her outside they'd faint! She has lightning speed and takes no messing from any of us cats, dogs or giant pheasants.

That is one place I don't lay blame, but the puppies . . . oh those silly faces fall for it time and time again. Sometimes they don't need any help. When Clover was a baby she pulled a bottle of champagne from the wine rack. It smashed on the tiles and we all had a drink. She had a hangover and cut paws. I just had the hangover. When Bracken first came into our madhouse, she was terrified of her reflection in the oven door. Jenny used to leave a tea-towel hanging to cover it. She ripped five to shreds before Jenny just let her get on and frighten herself. She still barks at the oven door, but only when it is clean and sparkly, which isn't very often.

I suppose I will have to wait until the kittens are full size before I let them take the blame for something I have done. At the moment they are so cheeky it looks like it will be the other way round.

I'm not having that!

Branching Out

8 July

All right, I admit it! I was stuck up a tree. But I wasn't the only one, that Jenny was waving around in the breeze just beneath me.

She said she had come up to rescue me, but don't believe a word of it, she can't let me have any peace or enjoyment.

It was a bit of a surprise when I ran after a fluffy-tailed squirrel which jumped to another tree when it reached the top. It disappeared from view but there was nowhere for me to go. The ground was an awfully long way down.

Jenny said she heard my desperate miaowing from the kitchen where she was toasting crumpets. I was actually singing, the view was worth praising in my melodic voice. I could see over a church, the top of our garage and next door's washing. Did you know he wears long, fleecy underwear?

I would have come down at my own pace when I'd had enough spying on the neighbours, but no, Jenny came panting up behind me gasping for breath and calling, 'Booby-doos, don't worry, mummy is here.'

Well I wasn't worried until she arrived clinging and wobbling, with leaves stuck in her hair and scratches all over her arms. She was clutching at me and spoiling everything, so I jumped on to the fence and then behind the lilac.

Jenny didn't come down. In fact she stayed up there for two hours. I licked the butter from the crumpets, knocked them to the floor for the puppies and then stuck my paw into the strawberry jam. It was great. I had a sleep on the new sofa and only woke when she started singing about the view herself, only she didn't seem to like it, she was trilling, 'Oh, it's so awful up here. Somebody . . . anybody, help!'

I went outside and had a look. Her bottom doesn't half look big in those jeans and with her legs wrapped around a tree trunk. I don't know why she stayed up so long, it was getting dark.

Headlights filled the drive and Ross was home. I ran to him for a cuddle. It was a good, ear-rubbing one, so when Jenny started on with that song again, I purred extra loud so that he couldn't hear.

Ross switched on the kitchen lights and I gave him the where's-my-dinner-then rub.

'Sorry Bluebell, don't know where the tin opener has got to. You'll have to wait till Jenny comes in. Where on earth has she gone, leaving the place in such a mess?'

No dinner! I had little choice, I ran to the door so he'd let me out into the back garden. He heard the screaming then. She soon ran out of songs.

It was great. He got out a ladder and I went up the tree again, the easy way. I had to get down quickly this time or he would have stood on my paws.

Jenny spent what was left of the evening on the sofa, so I sat on her tummy going up and down with the snores. She was too upset to think about the tin opener so Ross and I had fish and chips whilst he praised me for showing him where Jenny was.

She takes some looking after I can tell you.

After that she learned to use a ladder but we both stayed away from trees for quite a while. I didn't think the kittens would dare to climb up something so big when they were so little but they would have to learn eventually. As usual, I would give them the advantage of my considerable experience.

The chance came sooner than I expected.

I was on Jenny's knee as she was ordering a take-away. She was telling the man how to get to Ha'penny Hollow with his 'Flying Pizza', whatever that is.

'Turn left at that bush with all the pink blossom, bend with the road where the lovely white pussy cat always sits

and you know when you reach that house with the door newly painted in heavenly blue . . . turn right. We are the house with more lavender bushes than next door.'

'Can I speak to someone more sensible please?', the exasperated voice filled mine and Jenny's ears.

'Cheek!' she said, handing Ross the phone.

He spoke in a way as close to that of a sensible person as he possibly could. He guided the delivery man by pubs. They were both happy with that.

I hung around hoping for a lick of pizza crust but it had chilli on.

My first time with chilli was also my last. I had one tongue touch and ran at a million miles an hour out of the flap and up a tree without even thinking. I was there for ages. Jenny said it served me right for pinching human's food so she wouldn't come with any help.

That was winter and I was very cold. I thought of that branch now and how high it was. I wondered why my weight hadn't brought the tree down or at least the branch – the higher you get the thinner the branches.

I didn't want to risk it again but I remembered everything about the journey and the climb. It took only seconds, yet I was so scared every little thing stuck clearly in my mind.

The kittens ambled in, drawn by the smell. I told them not to bother, they'd end up on thin twigs. But they were bored. I asked them if they wanted to have the best view of a lovely summer's evening that was possible.

Farthing and Dandelion suddenly went wide-eyed with wonder. There weren't many places they hadn't explored around here. Something new was exciting.

I didn't want to go up there again so I told them the way. We had perfected our mental communication and with the help of a few chirrups and a couple of nose points they were off.

I knew they'd be going through my directions in their little heads.

'Past the black plastic bin that always smells of fish, up the winding path which pushes gravel between your toes, around the bush where that horrible tomcat sprays every night and on to the wall where we watch the hedgehog hunting slugs. Across to where we lay on the bluebells, right through to where we squashed the forget-me-nots. Stop at the mouse-hole where we always stick our paws in right up to our shoulders but never find anything. Just behind is a fat tree with bark where those busy ants live. Start climbing just beside the ivy leaves where we pounce on sunbathing bees.'

I knew they'd be there together and could see in my mind's eye as they continued past a branch that looked like Jenny's arms when she was throwing them about in a cross mood. I'd directed them to the higher branch which had leaves sticking out all over like Ross's hair on a windy day.

I went to sleep then and forgot about them.

When I woke it was dark, and Jenny was prodding me with an urgent finger.

'Bluebell! We haven't seen the kittens for hours and they haven't come in for supper. Do you know where they are?'

My first reaction was to rush to the food bowl and scoff the lot. Jenny wasn't letting me off the cushion until I helped. I was keen because she stood in the way of that chopped-up liver, the smell of which was wafting around the house. I wasn't going out, so I would try to get through that thick skull of hers. I went through the directions again mentally, very quickly. Do you know, she didn't even thank me!

'Oh Bluebell, you are no use! I suppose I'll have to find them myself.'

She went out then and I jumped on to the windowsill. Amazingly, she followed the exact route those kittens had taken!

As I ate, I saw her stout shoes and the bottom of a ladder pass the cat-flap. Minutes later Farthing and Dandelion joined the rest of us cats at the food bowls.

I should have told Ross, then I'd have had more liver. He would never have understood. There are no pubs on the way to the walnut tree.

Cat of Many Tongues

18–20 July

Jenny says she is going away to a conference, whatever that is!

I tried to look blank so she'd explain, but it didn't work. She didn't seem to notice any difference.

When I heard the phone ring I hung around at her feet so I could listen.

'Yes, the whole weekend we have to sit around the table discussing this matter until it's resolved.'

Is that it? She has to go away to sit and talk all day. She does that most of the time here anyway! Why does she have to go away to do it?

'Now Bluebell, you lot will be well looked after by a new lady, so I want no antics.'

I didn't want a new lady. I wanted Rachel who had looked after us for years in Yorkshire. She was my friend and she let me get away with anything.

How could I understand what these Lincolnshire people said? It took me two years to learn Yorkshire accents after only just understanding the Geordie Jenny spouts. Why the human race doesn't get together and decide to speak in one way we could all understand, I don't know.

There are some perks to being abandoned for a weekend. Jenny displays her guilt by buying up the deli at the supermarket. She had arranged several little tubs in the fridge. All had been scribbled on in a felt-tip pen. Some had 'Bracken and Clover' on them, others 'Willow and Bramble' or 'Farthing and Dandelion', but they all had 'Bluebell' in the biggest writing. I like everything! And even if I don't, I'm having my share.

Just as she shut the fridge door, leaving me drooling and curious, that horrible front doorbell interrupted the feast my imagination was having.

'Do come in,' Jenny said trying to sound posh by covering up her Geordie accent.

Now I heard what Jenny asked and I could hear someone called Pat talking, but I haven't a clue what she actually said. All I could hear was a lot of garble and rolling 'r's liberally dressed with 'Yes my love's.

Was this lady foreign? Did she know what English cats ate?

I knew then I was in for a weekend of problems. I wouldn't make life easy for a person who seemed to have come from the moon.

'I will introduce you to my little treasures,' I heard Jenny saying with that smile in her voice she keeps for trying to make an impression.

She clicked her tongue twice which is a universal call for puppies and cats to abandon all to rush to her side. There was a great scatter of claws on tiles and much OOOhing and AAAhing. I could imagine shoulders being patted, ears being rubbed and the proud look on Jenny's face as she showed off the loves of her life. I was staying put.

'Boobies! I must show you Bluebell, she is amazing!'

I heard the puppies dash into the kitchen first in their true sycophantic we'll-show-you way. Only they didn't find me. 'Cos they couldn't. I was off!

I might stay in the garden all weekend until Jenny and Ross return and feel so sorry they make it up to me for weeks.

I was only around the corner, and from the cat-flap I could hear the squeak of the hinge on the cupboard door where the cat food is kept. I could also hear Pat's 'Uh huh,

right!' So those words were the same in Lincolnshire. Either that or she'd made a special effort.

I stayed out. A huff in the garden is better than the rush in the house whenever Jenny has to pack a suitcase. She has six outfits to wear for two days, Ross always complains as he heaves the bags into the car.

'But I might be pale, I don't know what the light is like in London. And what if someone else has the same outfit?'

He gives in. He's heard it all before. He'll make his usual quip, 'It would be easier if you grew fur!' but always when she is in the car and out of earshot.

'What dear?' she will say.

'Oh nothing,' he lies. 'I just said it will be an easy drive, not too far.'

Then they leave with half her wardrobe and the contents of her entire dressing table. But none of us relax then. We know, with the certainty of left-out butter being licked, that after a few minutes the car will skid back up to the door, Ross will tear upstairs and return clutching a pair of earrings Jenny simply couldn't live without in London.

As usual there was lots of food and water all over the place. Our minder wouldn't start her activities until the morning and I'd be gone by then, under the compost heap where it is warm and smelly and lots of decaying bits stick to fur and, later, to cushions.

I was woken at eight by a big lady with a big voice. I was in a prone position on the draining board sleeping on a clean tea-towel that had been left out. There was no escape. I was rubbed and dubbed till ecstasy robbed me of my senses. Pat talked as she let the puppies into the garden, chattered all the time she filled their bowls and babbled as she heaved lids from tins for us cats.

I stayed on my vantage point. I wasn't rushing for stuff that we got every day. I had seen what was in the fridge.

I turned my back to feign disinterest. Pat came to fuss over me. She seemed to talk in a mixture of Greek, Chinese and English. I recognised bits like 'my pet', and 'Bluebell' but not much else. When the others were out chasing their tails in the garden, I heard the fridge door open. I turned around then.

Pat was nice. The more I listened, the more I understood this Lincolnshire way of speaking. Some words were the same like 'fresh prawns', and 'rare roast beef'. She didn't mind me licking her fingers and she cleaned up sick with one sweep of kitchen paper.

I decided to charm her. She talked and talked and talked. I listened; after all I had to live in this county so I would have to learn how the locals communicated.

When Jenny and Ross returned on Sunday evening I was happy to see them but sad to see the last of all the tasty bits in the deli cartons.

There was no way I could tell Jenny that I had learned the local lingo and was therefore not likely to try to run home to Yorkshire ever again. But she knew I was happier.

Later, as I sat on her lap picking dry mud from between my toes, she caressed my ears.

'You know Bluebell, I am so glad you like Pat. I was worried she'd get it wrong. She's just moved into the village too, from Cornwall. I couldn't understand a word she said. Funny accent that, charming though, just like the local way of speaking. Tomorrow we'll have a visit from the Lincolnshire carpenter. Let's hope he'll teach us how to understand this accent.'

All that effort and I still couldn't communicate locally!

Still, I've heard learning new languages keeps your brain supple.

At this rate mine will be doing aerobics.

The Foodie

Jenny has been cooking.

'I don't want any hairy cakes or slobber soup so you puppies and cats can go out into the garden!'

I got away with it by hanging particularly limp when she picked me up.

'Still got a poorly tummy Bloobies? You stay there then, under the table. But one move, mind, and you're out!'

She slammed down a big cookery book from which she had promised to make Ross something since he spent a fortune on it at Christmas. I smelt coffee before she sat down and thrust toes, painted pink at the ends and clinging desperately to rubber flip-flops, right up my nose. I daren't move. She would discover that I wasn't ill, just lazy.

She always reads aloud as she copies down recipes. I listened with half an ear, because if the food is a failure we little darlin's get it all to eat. She hates wasting anything. Usually she throws together anything she has in the cupboards and calls it dinner. That's why Ross bought the book.

As she droned on my ears pricked up. Where would she get the ingredients from for such dishes? I was in the fridge before breakfast and there was only a tin of half-eaten beans, two cracked eggs and some cheese with whiskers longer than mine.

'Shepherd's Pie. No, too common, we had that last year,' she said, flicking the pages irritatingly loudly. 'Toad-in-the-hole? No. No toads. Devils on Horseback, Savoury Ducks, Welsh Rarebit, Pigs in Blankets?' I really did feel sick now.

This wasn't cooking, this was a walk in the countryside. How could she eat these things, never mind find them in our less-than-stocked kitchen? What has suddenly become the matter with tins and packets? She feeds us out of them and for the first time in my life I'm glad. Faggots in gravy were being considered now. She'd probably just lick the gravy off like I do with my cat food sometimes.

I had to move. A romp around wet plants was preferable to hearing what horrible things poor Ross would have to eat tonight.

She stood up then. I met her white legs at the cooker. Was it going to be like Mothers' Day when she got out of cooking by setting her apron on fire?

I couldn't stand the tension and quickened my pace.

'Not going are you Bluebell? You haven't heard what I am making for dessert.'

I stopped then, knowing that the indulgent smile on her face meant it was something I would like (lots of cream and custard).

'Canary Pudding: it has lemons and cake, lots of sauce like you, and goes cheep.' She waved the wooden spoon menacingly.

I was out of there in a flash before feathers flew and she discovered a recipe for Miaow Mince.

I stayed out to enjoy a game of ripping a row of cabbages to shreds with the kittens. I don't know what she cooked in the end, but she can't have been proud of it; it wasn't in the fridge, I looked. There was nothing in there but a health hazard.

I remember once opening the fridge when everyone was in bed; I had the biggest feast of my life. There was a piece of beef, salmon with decoration all over it and a big bowl with trifle and cream brimming over the edges. Well it wasn't brimming for long. The muscles behind my tongue were worn out. My tummy was so full that I just licked everything else to get the flavour. I planned to wake up early for a bite of the beef and fish.

I thought I must have slept in when I heard voices in the

kitchen at seven o'clock. I went down to see Ross and Jenny eating toast and talking about 'the party'. It was to be a lunch on the lawn. I got smiles, a cuddle and a big bowl of biscuits so I knew they hadn't looked in the fridge yet.

I spent the rest of the day in the stable from where I couldn't hear screams of anger or someone else getting the blame.

When I get a look in the fridge I never pinch the vegetables, as I heard Jenny tell Ross to eat his greens so he'd have rosy cheeks. I won't eat toast either, as I hear if it's burnt it gives you curly hair. Can you imagine me with rosy cheeks and curly hair. What a mess!

I've had a go at the eggs though. They fell out when I got on to the top shelf. They smashed on the tiles and I licked a lot of the yolk up. I left some white and all the shells, but as it was a red hot day and Jenny was away, it cooked. When they were cleaning it up I heard them discuss a paw-proof lock, whatever that may be.

I might have to rely on my considerable charm or the puppies.

On second thoughts, I'll stick to my winning ways. Those puppies have bigger appetites than me; if I teach them my fridge-opening secrets they might clear out the shelves, not that that matters much if this terrible standard of contents continues.

You'd think people with such lovely cats would have some decent food in the fridge. All fur coat and no kippers!

Post War

12 August

I never thought I'd say this.

There is someone I don't like. I don't know how Jenny can allow them to step on to the same gravel as me, but she just laughs. This horror-of-the-universe replaces someone I was fond of in a 'poor soul' sort of way. Someone who respected me as superior in looks and worldliness. Someone who gave me a little titbit before they shoved masses of letters through the letter-box and on to our hall carpet.

That dear old postman has gone off to the greatest sorting office of them all, Jenny says. He has been replaced by some sort of punk person. I think it's a girl but the hair gives no clues and neither does the temperament. Evil is what I'd call it, both the appearance and the manner, to which I will never become accustomed.

For a start the delivery time has changed. Probably Miss Punk has to stop to polish her safety pins and frighten old ladies with her orange hair at every turn. For months now at exactly eight o'clock a little whistle made me perk up as I sat behind the front door. Then a delicious morsel of chicken or whatever was left over from dinner the previous evening would gently ease through the letter-box and into my mouth. Then and only then would the letters flutter to the ground way past me. If there was a parcel, Tommy would knock gently and Jenny would open the door. I would be cooed over, tickled and generally worshipped as the poshest cat hereabouts. He had a limp, with one shoulder lower than the other after fifty years of bag carrying,

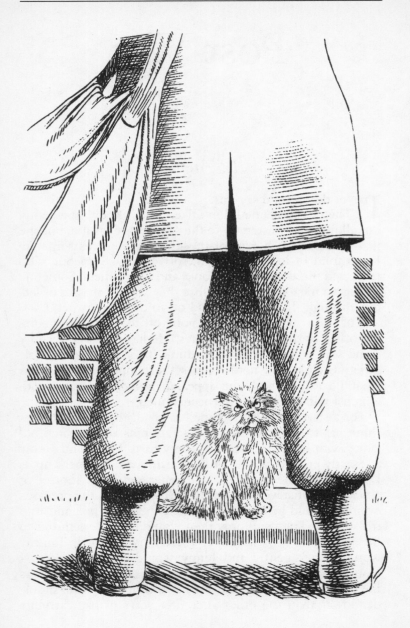

and a ginger moustache, but he was gorgeous and I would have told him so if he didn't already know I loved him.

But now it is quite a different story. Loud radio throbs down the street together with the big black boots, and then sharp-edged letters clatter through. I got beaten up twice by big brown envelopes before I realised what was happening. No little tasty bits from the other side to tempt me, only black-painted fingernails and a loud shock.

Next morning a piercing ring of the doorbell followed by a 'Sign here, duck' interrupted our morning coffee at ten thirty. It was the first time I saw her and the last time I wanted to.

'What's that then?' she said, looking down at me with a lip that curled up to her diamond-studded nose. 'An exploded pillow!'

Jenny thought it was funny. 'No, that's Bluebell.'

'Bluebell! More like a rat in a fur coat.'

Obviously pleased with what she mistook for humour, she shook the metal jewellery she'd used to liven up the uniform the Post Office had made her wear. 'Not very scary for a wild animal, are you!'

She went off down the path roaring with laughter. Jenny says I'm not to take it too seriously. But you know this has got me thinking and the plan I've come up with would please any wild animal.

It involves sharp teeth and black-painted fingernails. And someone I don't like.

Soggy Bottom

23 August

Saturday was hot. Jenny and Ross had gone off for the day to a wedding whatever that is. Sounds stupid, you have to wear big floppy hats and flowers on your bosom. I'm glad I wasn't invited.

We were left for the day and usually I like that. I get a good rummage through the drawers they leave open in their hurry and they always rush off without replacing the lids on the marmalade and peanut butter. But this time it was different.

Peanut butter makes me thirsty so I drank most of my water in one big slurp. I wasn't worried as the puppies always get extra to go with those boring bone-shaped biscuits. After a blissfully shout-free scoot up the plum tree, a tear around the vegetable plot and a couple of hours snooze on the sun lounger, I was hot. Very hot, my throat made a scrapy sound when I tried a little miaow.

I dragged my lazy body through the flap and flopped deliciously on to the cool tiled floor. Water was all I could think of.

When I ambled over to the puppies' bowls I screamed. They were all empty! The greedy guts hadn't even left slops around for everyone to skid on.

The sight of those dry bowls made me even more desperate. As you know, my brains equal my considerable beauty so I had to make them work for me and my thirst. I checked all the cat dishes. Willow, Bramble and the kittens had polished those off as expected. I walked along the bench to the sink to see if there was any water dripping

from the tap, which usually happens when Jenny's been in a mad dash. Just my luck. It was turned off tight, Ross must have made the tea.

I nudged at the door of the washing machine and jumped in. I wasn't in the mood for all that swinging about. I came out dizzy . . . and thirsty.

The hunt was on. I sniffed the air and that led me to a vase of flowers on the coffee table. They were very tall flowers and had drunk most of their water. My tongue couldn't reach and neither could my paw. I climbed up to stick my head in amongst those slimy stalks and leaves. I got the water then . . . all over my head and the carpet which drank it all immediately. None went into me. A few drips stayed on my coat but when I licked them they tasted horrible. I needed water even more!

I followed a trail of towels into the shower. No drips here – the heat must have taken care of what usually hangs around all day. But there, right beside me was a great big bowl where I have seen water before. It had a lid on but I could just wiggle my paw into the gap enough to get into it. I drank and drank. I wouldn't tell the puppies where the water was when I got out – only I couldn't get out. As I turned to jump on to the carpet the lid closed. The wood was too heavy. I tried with my bottom and my head but it just wouldn't move. I'd had enough to drink, had had enough of water and now I had to sit in it for the rest of the day.

It was dark when the car in the drive woke me, though I hadn't got much sleep with a wet bottom.

I heard a mad scrabble and Jenny said something about too much champagne as she lifted the lid of the toilet seat and nearly sat on me.

Her face scrunched as she watched me drag my soaked body across the floor.

'Yes,' she muttered. 'Definitely too much champagne.'

In the kitchen the puppies and cats were all enjoying fresh cool water with their suppers. I walked straight past into the garden. If I never saw water again I wouldn't care. I'm water total from now on.

The Needle Man

2 September

I had a pain in my ear so Jenny got out the basket, stuffed me in it (against my wishes) and drove me off to the town.

What a lot of noise! Everything is fast there, people, traffic and litter in the wind. We pulled into a car park and I knew I was at the vet's. He is the one who sticks needles in me so I said I wasn't going in, but Jenny ignored me. She just picked up the rickety handle and I was bounced through the door and plonked on the floor.

YUK! There were dogs everywhere. Strange dogs I'd never met before. I showed them all my teeth in a sweep-around-the-room hiss. That got them, they were shaking in their collars.

'Don't be silly Bluebell,' Jenny scolded. 'They aren't scared of you. It's the needle man who's made them so nervous.'

Why did she have to remind me! She put my basket on the padded seat so everyone had a good view of me. I hated it. As usual I could hear lots of 'Ooh, she's gorgeous. What a lovely face!' in the background but I couldn't enjoy it because a beige dog with wire for hair was staring right at me.

'Oh look, Tilly has fallen in love with your cat,' cried the lady who was holding the black-nosed brush on a lead.

No thanks. That dog's stare was not of fondness but menace.

I curled into a ball and stared at the back of the basket so I was invisible but I could see through the slats. There

119

was a spaniel with a big grubby bandage on its paw and an odd-looking thing coughing its lungs out. It must be because of those fag things Jenny is always complaining about.

One by one they were dragged into the needle room so I stopped being invisible, turned around and wow! It was my turn to be in love. There, on a new lady's lap was a Westie puppy, all white fluff and cuteness. How could I ask Jenny to get me one?

'She's gorgeous.' Jenny said. 'What's her name?'

The lady smiled and snuggled into the lovely face.

'Colin.'

Can you believe it? That's the same name as that dreadful man who throws stones at us when we dig his seed beds. Jenny throws all her slugs and snails into his garden. I went off the idea and looked out of the window. There was a van

pulling up with a black and white kitten driving. He was looking over the wheel and a man with long hair was sitting behind him. When they'd parked a lady with flowing clothes and dreadlock hair came in.

'New-Age has fallen off a wall, he's limping. I'll sit in the van until my turn as we don't have a box.'

New-Age's injury didn't stop him climbing all over the seats, swinging on the sun visors or chewing all that incredible hair of its owners.

Our name was called and I gathered my strength to make a run for it. But I didn't have to. No needles just drops in the ears and a cuddle.

That's a new one.

Jenny said I was a hero who charmed everyone. That's not a new one.

Blobby Bodies

13 September

How come people think they're beautiful?
Today Jenny and Ross spent most of their time in front of a mirror. I don't know what they saw staring back at them as they tried on all the clothes in the wardrobe, but I know the truth.

People are like uncooked pastry. Pale and blotchy, bulgy and blobby.

I bet they wish they could roll themselves out to a new more attractive shape and toast themselves in the oven like a muffin.

But they can't, they are stuck with this unattractive shape for ever. How do they deal with it? By covering themselves with expensive and awful clothes.

They must have been going somewhere special. One of those invitation things was given pride of place above the fireplace and fingered every few days. Jenny said she couldn't believe her luck and Ross was glad that he might be mixing with the men who run the country. Usually he is arguing with them as they speak on TV, but he can't be any good – they never answer back!

Jenny had spread all their clothes on the bed after a frenzy of tummy tucking and zip tugging. They had changed from white and wobbly to red and rolling.

'It's OK for you Bluebell,' Jenny said as she lifted me off some particularly soft silky creation I'd been plodding on with my paws. 'You are always perfectly dressed and never have to worry.'

I was glad she noticed. I get lots of admiration for my coat. People love to run their fingers through my hair. If only they knew it is all lick!

From my forced position on the floor I had an even better view. Ross had on a black suit with shining lapels and a white frilly shirt. His tie was a little bow of pink froth. I say he had the suit on but it was trying to burst off . . . back into the dusty old trunk he'd taken it from. Jenny gave him that look she usually saves for something nasty on the carpet.

'Very sixties dear. Take it off!'

When he did I noticed the seat of his trousers was shiny to match. He was perspiring, his acres of flesh seemed to be expanding.

One of the reasons Jenny loves us little darlin's is that we don't need clothes. All that ironing in the basket under the stairs! We tell her it's too high by falling off it. Only then does she switch on a black and white movie, open a box of chocolates and get the ironing board out.

We have to walk beneath hosts of shirts which Ross never knew he had but will hang around on doors all day until he comes home. Only when he has admired her hard work and rewarded her with a gin and tonic will she ask him to hang them in the wardrobes.

'I don't know where you keep them all,' she says from the sofa, lying. Ross's eyes glow with the excitement of not having to pretend he doesn't mind wearing the same shirt two days running.

They had been in the bedroom for hours. Bramble and Willow had joined me in the search for the cosiest item of clothing discarded on to the floor. Farthing and Dandelion had wrapped themselves in something see-through; like dumplings in clingfilm.

At that moment we were testing a pair of velvet hipsters which Willow favoured but I still preferred the bounce of that shrunken angora minidress. Bramble, being little, frequently disappeared beneath some tossed-aside shirt or was hit on the head by a black plunge bra.

It was hard to see the carpet for horrible things these

people actually wore in public in the past. I was so glad I didn't know them then.

The puppies bounded in wanting their walk.

'My God!' Ross cried snatching a look at his watch. 'What time is it?'

It was three o'clock and Jenny decided Bracken and Clover would have to make do with a run in the garden. They needed to get into town before the shops shut.

Us cats were left in the bedroom, which itself was left in a flurry of last-minute panic by two people wanting to impress and having nothing to wear.

I rolled around having a claws-out play fight with Bramble on a chiffon purple concoction and Willow de-tatted her entire body on to black velvet.

We had a sleep all cosily tangled in fluorescent flowery material and then went downstairs for some biscuits. On the way past the living room I noticed they'd left a window open and the curtains were billowing in the breeze. That invitation card they were so thrilled with was on the floor. I went to sniff at it. It had a gold edge and smelt of dust. I was surprised it was so stiff after they had handled it so much. But then I realised they hadn't handled it enough. It was they who would have the surprise when they came home.

It was dusk. They swept in in a flurry of expensive bags and parcels.

I miaowed at them like mad so that they would come into the living room to read the invitation.

'Shut up Bluebell, we are in a mad dash!'

I wouldn't give in. This was much too important.

She came in, so surely she would see the invitation and realise.

'Oh, we left the window open. Thank you Bluebell, you are clever.'

Not clever enough. The only bit of her that came into contact with the invitation was the sole of her shoe.

She dashed upstairs then to cause a tornado of whipped-off clothes and shampoo.

I had to get them to see the invitation.

I picked up the card between my teeth, not without discomfort. It bent twice on the stair edges and seemed to make my mouth grow at the corners; it was a strain but I soldiered on.

Ross was out of the shower smelling strongly of girl's

stuff. I dropped the card at his feet, trying not to look up at the horrible sight.

'Thank you Bluebell. We will need that when we go to this special party.' He needed it now. To read properly! But he didn't.

I sat on the dressing table giving Jenny the occasional paw tap as she plastered stuff on to hide every inch of her face. I made a mistake by nudging her when she was holding that wand that makes her eye-lashes look like spiders' legs. She knocked me to the floor, blaming me for the black streak down her cheek.

I gave up then. Left them to it.

I lay in the hall but couldn't sleep as I didn't want to miss the excitement that was sure to follow.

They swept past me in a cloud of silk and perfume. I heard the gravel crunch, the car doors slam, and I waited.

Not long. The door was flung open. New shoes sped past me and up the stairs only to return seconds later. They'd forgotten the invitation.

The car engine started up. I'd count to ten.

The door was flung open again and they flew past me in a frenzy of accusations and blame.

It was quiet in the hall but I knew it wouldn't be in the bedroom so I waited for the show to come to me.

When it did, it was an extravaganza of bad taste. Shiny suits, floaty frocks all creases, cat hairs and snags.

Jenny elbowed Ross out of the way.

'Why didn't you tell me it was fancy dress?'

'You should have read the invitation properly!'

She didn't admire my fur then . . . it was all over her party outfit.

As I said, people are not attractive.

I got Bramble and Willow together to go upstairs. The light was left on so we got a good look at their new clothes and the price tags. They'd spent a fortune.

But it was worth it, we all had a comfy sleep on material we'd never felt before. Pity I hadn't been out in the muddy garden like the others.

Looking Down

23 September

Can't they take care of this house?

I have been investigating a funny smell for months. Do they take any notice of what I am trying to tell them? No!

I could have saved them a fortune and the indignity of having to explain a hole in the kitchen ceiling to everyone from the milkman to the Avon Lady.

The bathroom is somewhere they always throw me out of. I didn't know why, until I saw them one day with no clothes on. What a sight! I don't think I will ever take them seriously again. All I have to do when they are telling me off is remember that terrible day and all the sting has gone out of their proud indignance.

When they are out I go to lots of places; they are hopeless at shutting anything: doors swing, drawers gape and cupboards display their tired goods like a man in a dirty raincoat.

Do you know, that Jenny has seventeen bras. Seventeen! What for, for goodness sake? She still doesn't own one of those jumpers with the big bumps he loves so much in other women's jumpers.

I have left hairs on every bit of clothing they own.

Why?

Because it's there of course.

I have been drawn to the bathroom of late because of a smell.

It is not unpleasant, rather like the toilet end of a mouse-hole. But I knew it shouldn't be there behind the wall where the water from the shower disappears. All the time, after that getting-wet stuff they do every morning, there was a quiet drip. They have such poor hearing and smell I don't know how they get around. No wonder they never catch mice. It must be all that perfumed body gel they are so liberal with. That and clouds of powder fill the bathroom every morning. Dulls the senses.

If it hadn't, they'd have noticed the smell getting stronger. Six times I had been bodily ejected from that room when I had been sniffing in a very pointed way. They had to wait for the water to eat through the plaster so that it fell into their breakfast cornflakes.

Everyone got a shock but me. Jenny screamed, Ross swore and the puppies leapt two feet into the air. I had the advantage of knowing what the cause was, so I ran upstairs and peeped through the hole at their gaping mouths.

'What has Bluebell done now?'

I couldn't believe it. I was getting the blame for this too?

When Ross investigated he looked down the hole with me.

'Hmph. This is nothing to do with you this time,' he admitted, poking at stinky, wet plaster.

That was when two tons of the stuff fell on to Jenny as she was trying to save the toast and marmalade. She wasn't happy. She had to catch a train that morning and had her new expensive suit on. I know it was new because it had no hairs on it yet.

I watched her clean up. Just herself. She wouldn't help Ross with the mess as she blamed him for poor house maintenance, forgetting for a moment that it is she who spends hours in the shower with hot water massaging her shoulder muscles twice a day.

She went off in a rush.

Ross left two minutes later saying he'd try to be home an hour early to make a start on the disaster. He thought he'd shut everyone downstairs but as usual he couldn't be bothered to find where I was hiding. The puppies had a great time playing with the rubble. There wasn't an inch of

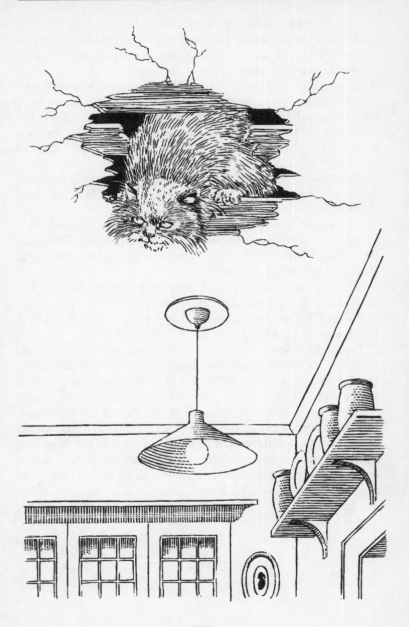

the kitchen they didn't toss bits of ceiling into. The other cats made chalky white footprints on every downstairs carpet and then spread out on the settees to pick lumps from between plaster-weighted paws. It was everywhere.

I waited until Bracken and Clover were asleep before I edged big lumps to balance on the edge of the hole above their littered baskets. When I had enough to cause the desired effect, I ran around knocking them all on to their dopey heads and snoring chests. They woke up and whooped around some more.

When we heard a key in the door we knew we'd be sorry. Jenny had expected the mess to be cleaned up. It was a hundred times worse!

She swore as she changed her clothes, then she swore as she threw us all out into the foggy, damp garden. Then she swore some more as she kept appearing at the dustbin with bags and curiously white hair.

Ross stayed out extra late and when he walked in the door there was more swearing.

I don't know how long we have to live like this but I think it won't be long.

Jenny has now discovered baths and spends hours in there with expensive oils and mud on her face. Ross nearly fainted when the water bill came in today; he made a phone call immediately.

I bet he wishes he'd listened to me when I tried to tell him there was a problem. Probably he wouldn't take much notice anyway. I have spent hours on top of the washing machine fine-tuning my ears to that strange new noise it is suddenly making. He has never stopped to glance at me. But I don't care, I'll keep on anyway. It's rather a thrill actually.

Total Imaginings

5 October

Why is Jenny so amazed at my psychic ability?

I have only allowed her to know a fraction of what I know and *she* thinks *I'm* clever!

I have always thought she was bonkers but now she is giving new evidence to make me think she is totally gone.

She has always known I have, along with the other cats, super hearing, smell and yoga ability. She read about psychic cats in *Your Cat* magazine and decided to do a test on me.

Well she went the wrong way about it.

I was sleeping and didn't want to wake from my dream involving Lucky, a big handsome black cat from across the road. She wanted to test the theories she'd just read in the magazine on her most intelligent cat. That was one time I wished Willow's main occupation wasn't sleeping and Bramble's wasn't mice.

She considered mine to be brain work.

What she didn't realise was that the others were cleverer at hiding their extraordinary psychic abilities. I was too open, too caring, too lazy. What is the point in covering up something wonderful to humans although common to us cats? None, I had thought, until she started to really take notice . . . and notes.

She wasn't having any of my can't-be-bothered, heap-on-the-sofa look, even though that was one I had really perfected over the years of living with this mad woman. No, she had the magazine in her hand and she was going for it. *Now!*

The article might have gone unnoticed had it not been for my display of awareness last Sunday evening.

They were late. She thinks I was worried and she was right! Worried about my food. Usually at six o'clock I am rewarded for my 'Teddy cuddle' as she weirdly calls it, with a choice of tasty delights.

She is always impressed when she shows me two tins at a time and I have a sniff then rub my cheek against the one I want. If I had something in gravy last time I choose something in jelly the next. She is as impressed as if I'd flown to the moon.

Why? I don't know.

I couldn't eat the same thing twice running, neither could she, so why is she so impressed?

Anyway, it was eight o'clock and my tummy wasn't just rumbling, it was positively volcanic.

They had taken Bracken and Clover with them to visit their friends for Sunday lunch as the house was near a wood. Dogs love woods. I love dogs to go in woods . . . there is always a chance they won't come out. It did cross my mind that that was what had happened and they had had to organise a search party for those silly puppies. But I knew . . . just knew that Jenny had drunk too much wine and fallen asleep. She can't drink during the day, but as she had spent more than usual on a bottle of wine (she only normally buys bottles with £1-off offers), she was determined to enjoy the wine she had taken for the lunch.

I strained my ears when I felt they were close by. I felt a sort of vibration in the ground that only their car made. I reckoned they were a mile away so I went out to the brick post that held the gate on. This is where she'd see my most strained, starving and neglected look at the earliest possible opportunity.

I saw the car, then I saw her mouth go. They stepped on the brakes right beside me. 'Bluebell you never, ever sit there! How did you know we were coming?'

Was she kidding! I *always* know. I know before her what she is going to wear each day too. I can tell the moment she opens her eyes whether she will spend the day covered in make-up and squeezed into tights pretending to be as posh as her friends or she will simply be herself, the village scarecrow.

It's important to my existence which she will be. She opens the door and greets everyone with a kiss and coffee or hides behind the sofa the minute she hears tyres on gravel. I like the 'Oh God, don't let them see me!' days best, as it's more peaceful and I don't have to show off my magnificence. I prefer a 'tummy to the sky' slob-out to having red-painted fingernails raked through my hair.

Later that evening, Jenny was staring at me trying to put her thoughts into my head. I received them the first time but she kept repeating and repeating, 'Give me a kiss Bluebell, give me a kiss!'

That is the last thing I would do to someone who had woken me up.

I ignored her and sent a thought back.

'GET LOST!'

I only sent it once but that was all I needed. She got up then turned on the telly and left me to my dreams.

She thinks it was her own idea.

Hope she doesn't read this!

No Sweat

9 October

Clean, clean clean! That's all I ever do. The other cats don't tidy up do they? Whose muddy paws do you think made this mess? Not mine, I can tell you.

I heard Jenny saying that we had some important guests coming. I'm proud of my house and like others to say how nice it is. They won't do that if they see this mess, will they? The only comments that will fly around will be ones of disgust.

It had rained for two days and that meant that Willow, Bramble and me had spent most of our time on the bed. I was woken by a wet fur smell, quite disgusting and unsettling. Two cats had gone outside for a walk around the seedbeds then jumped up here to annoy me.

I could hear the vacuum cleaner buzzing and that rousing classical music Jenny plays when she blitzes the whole house. No peace here, so I stretched and opened my eyes. Mud everywhere. It started quite faint on the white duvet beside those two sleeping cats and grew stronger and lumpier as I followed the trail to the landing, down the stairs and then across the kitchen floor where it lay in puddles and streaks. The cat-flap was filthy. Two delinquent kittens were jumping in and out, flicking mud at each other. I only had to narrow my eyes and they were off.

I heard the vacuum go off, then buckets and mops came into the kitchen before a sweaty and red Jenny.

'Ayeeee! Right Bluebell, you are the only cat up, so you must have made this mess all by yourself. Get out!'

The door was flung open and I was rushed through with the help of a floppy wet mop.

What a cheek. I was innocent.

On the step there was more mud, only it had started to dry. As I was the first one to master the cat-flap and taught the others the joys of making it rattle all night, I feel a special responsibility towards it. I felt ashamed to own this cat-flap right now. I heard a car draw up and posh voices grew nearer to the front door. I could still hear the music and knew Jenny was in the shower. The doorbell was ignored. The gravel crunched. The important guests were coming around to the back. I couldn't let them see my special entrance like this. Quickly, I rubbed my fluffy paw anywhere there was dirt.

The shining shoes arrived just as I was finishing.

'Oh look, Gerald. What a beautiful cat!'

Too late. I was whisked up on to a white silk blouse. My cleaning paw pressed hard on to the gleaming shoulder just beside the pearls.

I was lifted into the air and then cuddled close many times so that my mucky paws made an interesting pattern on that shiny material. Jenny opened the door, all lipstick and perfume. Her smile faded as she saw the visitor's clothes.

The shriek was worse than when I once chewed her anniversary bouquet.

I was off up the garden through all that mud myself. I didn't go back until it was dark.

So much for cleaning. I'm keeping my paws for what they were made . . . posing.

Cats are also made for windowsills. Or are windowsills made for cats?

I don't know which came first but they are perfect for each other.

I watched the kittens join Bramble to stare out of the window at the autumn leaves. The way their tails hung down they could have been fishing – if there had been any water. They wouldn't even need bait, they had their own wiggly bits at the end.

At that moment I was proud to be a cat. Such beauty looking at me, such minds looking out. I think that's what makes us so fascinating to people. They have neither.

I mean, what sort of person would be talking on the phone for hours, and when the caller says she must go as it is costing a fortune, say it is OK as she has them on her cheap rate for family and friends?

A Jenny sort of person, that's who! The caller fell for it too, never felt a thing; until the bill came in.

It really is a wonder we little darlin's are so sane.

The kittens have added to her madness of course. She is forever searching for them in the garden. These two tiny tabbies are sparrow coloured which makes them difficult to see against a background of gravel, soil or dead plants, which is all Jenny has out there at the moment. This camouflage gives them a ring of confidence to get away with things my blue body just couldn't chance.

The surprised face that Dandelion wears about the house earns him that unique attention moulded especially for shy, nervous cats. But out there he is a tearaway. Jenny just doesn't see it. He hides in, on, or beside the compost heap where everything is brown, black and waving about . . . just like him. He could be there for a week and she'd peer from the window (without the elegance of a well-hung tail), walk past him several times and panic twice as often.

We know where he is. We can see, hear and smell him. He is a little tinker out there in the real world. Jenny knows little about what really happens in life: she is too busy with books, telephones and making Ross's life a misery.

She misses out on real thrills like charging around the lawn at eighty miles an hour or the perverse excitement of 'finding the ugliest bug to gobble up without a wince' competition. She knows nothing of the thrill of pouncing on a sleeping dog, swinging on enormous underwear on washing lines or scattering through a just-raked pile of crisp leaves.

Mind you, the kittens come up with some tricks I have forgotten, like patting at anything dangling or fluffy, or pouncing on toes beneath a duvet. All these daft things I have never found remotely interesting since I thought it was clever to catch my own tail.

Jenny needs to get real. Even when she goes to the stable she is so single minded. Misses a lot of opportunities if you ask me. She has never climbed Raven's tail or stood on tiptoes on his back without a saddle. She misses out on exchanging air from the horse's nostrils and pouncing at hooves from beneath straw. Why does she have this horse for heaven's sake? It can't just be for throwing money at, which is what Ross says. I've never seen her do that actually, she tosses the odd carrot and even lumps of sugar but never coins or notes. Why should she? Raven doesn't know where the shops are either.

No, I think her real reason for having a horse is to sweat.

It must be so important to Jenny to sweat because to have a horse just for this purpose seems extravagant. Brushes are treated violently in this quest for perspiration; if she brushed me like that she'd have me eating hay too.

She rides up a nice dampness too. Raven runs round and round the paddock jumping over wooden poles and rubber tyres. He steams but Jenny keeps all her vapour in her jumper and just gets wet. Don't know why; it is the horse who is doing all the work.

I never sweat. Wouldn't dream of it.

Jenny doesn't have my breeding. Her perception of life is all wrong: she never puts aside time for lying on laps, licking her tummy or scratching sofas. She never even purrs for goodness sake. And what would be the point of her sitting on windowsills? She has no tail to speak of, even less of a mind to think with and just think of all that sweat! YUK!

Hard to Swallow

14–15 October

'I've had cat-hair sandwiches again!'
Ross was furious when he came home from work. He didn't even say hello to any of us. But his angry comment blanketed us all in blame.

I think it's Jenny's fault. She makes the packed lunch. Hair is nothing to do with us. We just grow it!

Ross got out a cloth and a bottle of disinfectant and began rubbing wildly at the work surface where Jenny always slaps wedges of cheese between even greater wedges of bread when she's watching breakfast TV. I had enjoyed a nap there after he'd left for work. I like a tasty cheese crumb now and again, but it is a bit much when you have to nibble your bed clean before you lie down.

I know we shouldn't be on there but that Jenny is too busy yakking on the phone before she goes shopping. It just happens that that is where she makes sandwiches and that it has the sunny patch when I'm sleepy.

After one of Ross's outbursts she will take care for a few days wiping and blowing in a most exaggerated manner. Then bags of shopping will be dumped, pots of plants watered, saddles polished and cats allowed a doze, all on his precious sandwich area.

But not while he is keeping an eye on her. Oh no! She will go to any lengths to get him off her shoulder whilst she is packing up his lunch. Once she even fixed it wearing yellow rubber gloves which she made a great display of taking from their sterile plastic wrapper. That only lasted one day because when she tried to wash dishes with them after lunch they leaked. Two fingertips were missing. There was only one place they could be. In egg mayonnaise in Ross's plastic lunch box. Perhaps, by now . . . in his tummy!

'Well Bluebell,' she said, as I rubbed against her ankles to join in her laughter, 'at least they were clean . . . and hairless! Be extra nice to him tonight Bluebell, just in case!'

We all were. The puppies lolloped and wiggled. Bramble, Willow and the kittens all got on his knee at once and I wrapped his shoulders in my silken body, whilst purring in his ear as I chewed his hair.

I don't know why he complains. Eating hair is second nature to cats. We love a good lick. We even collect a ball of it in our stomachs so that we can heave a great slimy sausage of it out in front of anyone squeamish. It's healthy fun! We don't make a fuss. He should be used to it by now. I don't think he has ever had a dinner, lunch or tea without a stray hair falling from some furry person in this house, even Jenny drops the odd hair. But he picks those out with great disdain as they're blonde and curly and so easy to spot. He settles then, thinks he has 'got it', but we know!

Jenny came in with a beer and a big bowl of nuts.

'Nice day, darling?'

'Not too bad, thank you.'

'Nice drive home?'

'Yes.'

'Nice lunch?'

'Mmmm.'

His mouth was full of nuts now, so we all relaxed. I tried not to think about his tummy being full of rubber fingertips.

She was back to normal next morning. We'd all had a swift cuddle and she'd carried the kittens downstairs, so tabby hairs were highly visible as they stuck out of her white towelling bath robe. The puppies put both paws on her chest while she rubbed them before letting them run in the garden.

She took bread from the bread bin and something from

141

the fridge. I jumped up to see what he was getting today. Wet, wobbly ham!

She thrust a bit beneath my nose and I gave it a polite lick.

Ross was still in the shower so she pretended to talk to him.

'Hair sandwiches dear. From the front, tummy or tail? A nice juicy whisker, perhaps a bit of grit from between the toes or . . . ?'

She heard his feet on the stairs and dropped me to the ground.

She had a pinny on and was washing her hands when he entered the kitchen door.

'Toast or cereal?'

He was reading the newspaper and crunching at something so hard even the milk couldn't get at it, so I went out then. When I came back, Jenny was off riding and I had a strong fancy for that bit of ham I'd licked earlier. I jumped up and everything was still there, everything, that is, except my bit of ham!

Well, he'd never know. Would he?

Fright Night

31 October

Have you ever seen a pumpkin?

Well if you have, you surely haven't seen one like mine!

All summer Jenny has been watering a big plant with even bigger fruits on it. I have pounced around beneath its leaves and I swear it has grown before my very eyes. At first I thought I'd found a little yellow ball the puppies had lost, then, as it grew, I realised this thing was attached to its leaves.

As the autumn crept up, the leaves which had shaded me and the incredible growing ball died back. There was a great ceremony when Jenny waved a knife at Ross and said, 'Right, tonight's the night we cut the pumpkin!'

He looked relieved and followed her out, so we all trooped out after them.

We didn't know how muscle-man-that-wasn't would lift it. It was a struggle, not helped by me winding myself around his legs as he staggered to the kitchen door.

I thought the bench would crack as he dropped it down so I got up to see. It was twice as big as me (but didn't have my breeding).

'Haven't we done well!' Ross sighed.

'Well *I* have!' Jenny corrected. 'You only cut it!'

'Isn't it beautiful?'

I had to agree, it was better than those tiddly little tomatoes they kept bringing in or the carrots in rude shapes. It was impressive, but what was it for?

144

Ross and Jenny started to heave and cut at it. I heard something about hard work and soup. I don't do either so I left.

My rumbling tummy woke me and it was quite dark so I had to be careful how I slithered down the tree. I was still a bit dopey as I ambled towards the door and that made the fright worse. I must have jumped two feet into the air without really trying when I saw the devil on the front step.

I knew it had come to get me as I really hadn't been good that week, what with licking the cream off the visitors' scones and letting the puppies take the blame amongst millions of other things.

The devil was in a fiery temper. He had triangular eyes with flames burning in them so I hissed at the pointed teeth waiting to spit fire at me. He wasn't going to get me! I would fight for my soul! Only I couldn't, I was frozen to the spot. I had to await my fate.

That was when the wind got up and blew the devil out. Do you know, it was the pumpkin with a stupid old candle inside! If my heart hadn't been beating so fast I would have laughed. Instead I biffed the lid off and hooked out the sad and now unscary candle. My paw felt warm so I followed it into the pumpkin which fitted around my body perfectly and I could see everything out of the triangles.

A car pulled up and Jenny opened the house door.

'Hello!' she called in a voice that had already had too much wine. 'The Halloween party's in here!'

Two people got out of the car and waved. As they came up the step they bent down to look at the pumpkin so I miaowed a welcome; only because of the way my body was curled and the enclosed space, it came out all wobbly and waily. There was an air-renting scream before the gravel scattered at the feet of a couple shouting that they'd seen Beelzebub himself. They sped off in the car leaving Jenny speechless for once.

For heaven's sake! They were even more scared than I was. I knew all along that it was just a candle.

Didn't they realise that it was just a sweet little pussy-cat's eyes?

Jenny hooked me out and shook me quite a bit.

'Why do you have to play these tricks on everyone Bluebell?'

I never did! All these tricks just happened. I would never plan to scare someone, except . . . well, that was only once. Then there was the time when . . . oh dear, now my memory has been jogged I can remember things I'd rather not.

Jenny rough-handled me into the kitchen where there was a big pan of soup bubbling on the stove. Every dog and cat dish was filled with yellow soup that had gone cold. It would be Jenny's first attempt. We were expected as always to chew through the lumps and lick up every last slimy bit. I sniffed at it. It smelled like me . . . all pumpkiny and burnt.

Clover and Bracken sat looking at it, they had joined Bramble and Willow in the 'I'm not touching that' sit-in. Jenny stomped along.

'Eat it up you lot! It's all there is.'

This was a lie as I'd seen sausages and steak. The puppies had smelt them too.

The doorbell rang and Jenny went to answer it. I only needed ten seconds. Two seconds for the jump, one for each piece of meat I hooked to the floor, and three for the getaway.

It was delicious. That soup never did get eaten but it blocked the sink up for a week before Jenny had to admit defeat. She never did notice the missing steaks, she had too many to start with. In fact by the end of that weekend we were all sick to death of them and would have given anything for a change. Even a little soup would have been welcome . . . but not pumpkin!

That little devil of a soup will not be welcome again in this house. The plumber's bill has made sure of that.

My Little Secret

3 November

A whole new world has opened up to me. A few weeks ago I was wandering around the garden sniffing the same boring old plants and rocks that have been there for ages when I saw something. Jenny had cut down a big climbing plant with a clump of stalks I couldn't see past before. There was this big glass room with plants and sofas. It was in a place called 'next door' where I'm not supposed to go. No wonder Jenny wants me to stay away, it's much better than here.

I looked around, my hair blowing in the freezing wind; no one was out but me so I sneaked through the new gap in the hedge. There was a window open so I took that to mean all cats were welcome. It was heaven. The sun shone through all that glass and warmed my cold bones to perfection. It was like being outside but the wind couldn't get to me.

There were three green-and-white striped cushions to choose from, so I had an hour on each.

I would have stayed until the sun went in but I heard a voice call, 'Robert, will you get my book from the conservatory please.' Then the door opened and I ran home back to that dead old fireplace with those annoying puppies.

I've been every day since and even get fed there now. One day a charming lady caught me in a flat-out, tummy-to-the-sky sleep.

'So this is the reason for all this grey fluff on my seats is it?' As her voice was soft, I gave her a leg rub and she was as hooked as everyone is with my charm. She called me 'my little company' as I sat on her lap every afternoon and ate salmon or prawns from her crustless sandwiches.

Just as I was thinking of never going home again, the doorbell rang and I heard Jenny's angry voice shake through the house to my little ears.

'Have you kidnapped my Bluebell, my darling?'

I was so embarrassed. In she rushed, showing me up with those tatty jodhpurs and wild hair. She grabbed me in the most undignified manner and cuddled me so close I almost choked. 'This is a very special cat. A pedigree of the highest breeding and intelligence. And she's mine!'

I was bounced out of 'next door' and placed on a new cushion beside the blazing log fire. Willow and Bramble just looked on as I ate minced steak. It was good to be appreciated. I was getting my nose pushed out since that monster of a horse came to live with us. But if that Jenny thinks a bit of flattery is all it takes to keep me from the sunniest sleeping spot ever, she must keep her brains in her riding boots.

The only thing that has changed is that I make sure I come back before Jenny does. Oh and my new name. It's 'my little secret' now and that's the way I'm going to keep it.

At least from that hooligan Jenny. I think I might show the kittens how to improve their lives though. Let Jenny have the heebie-jeebies when they give their affections to another. Farthing and Dandelion could do with some structure. We've been worn out with their sheer energy.

The older they get, the more I realise that is all it is: sheer energy. They have no skill, no purpose to life.

I suppose being rescued kittens who left their mummies too soon did rob them of feline education, so I have watched them and come up with a great plan.

I, with my accomplishments over the years of perfecting how to get the most out of life, will take them in paw. A sort of governess.

Yes, I like that idea. Passing on one's profound thinking and worldliness. After all they still haven't been out of the house and garden. They wouldn't know a mouse from a dinosaur or a stick of rhubarb from a stick of dynamite.

They have already proved their intelligence by analysing the various looks in my eye to judge whether or not they can use me as a trampoline, though I have also had to develop a strong line of communication in the smack-on-the-nose department.

You see they have very simple basic faults which result in not getting as many treats or cuddles as they could. For instance, when they smell cooking they run to the kitchen just like the rest of us. Then what do they do? Jump up and down on the work top ending up with a rough grab and a drop to the cold tiles.

That's not what it's about, is it? I am going to show them how to sit just behind Jenny's feet as she is stirring something delicious. That is where any kitten is bound to be stood on. The shock is only brief, but worth it for the big cuddle that follows, with nuzzling, stroking and whispering into the neck fur and always . . . yes, always, a gift of

something tasty, usually only served to Ross on a big plate next to a bottle of wine.

I have been watching Farthing and Dandelion's behaviour with house guests too. They waste every chance for fun. They hang around people who like cats instead of getting screams and sneezes from those who protest they don't. These folk have so much to learn it is our duty to irritate them into loving us. I am going to demonstrate to the kittens how to make someone freeze rigid, simply by jumping on to their lap as they raise a cup of tea to their mouths. These are the ones who should leave with muddy paw-marks and fur all over their clothes, not the ones who love us already.

Wasting opportunities to get back at Jenny when she is stomping around and being too busy for us has to be dealt with; also, the kittens are too thoughtful in being sick in the garden. What is wrong with the sofas and cream rugs? A trail of dinner there always stops her ignoring us.

If Jenny is in the kitchen talking with friends, the best way to get noticed is to walk all over the table. Now, she knows and I know that I often sit there to watch the bird table, but she will stroke me on her lap for ages to keep me off whilst telling guests who are examining the biscuits for hairs, 'I don't know what got into her, Bluebell has never been on the table before!'

Farthing and Dandelion are always being thrown off the beds, especially when the extra cosiness of a turned-back duvet is asking for it. I will show them how to stop those grabbing hands that plop them to the floor by simply looking all sweaty and unkempt. Jenny thinks we are running a temperature and wants us to sleep it off as it is cheaper than vet's bills. Never fails!

I am working on a training programme to teach kittens how to obtain a feast. At the moment they are so thrilled and grateful for anything placed in their bowls. Gobbling this enthusiastically never leads to any sort of banquet. At first it is hard on a rumbling tum to sniff and ignore dinner. But they will see that if they turn their noses up another tin will be opened, boxes shaken, chickens stripped and mince cooked. I love the panic on Jenny's face as she thinks I'm ill or the food is off. In the end she shouts, 'Oh, please yourself Bluebell,' then wanders off.

Willow, Bramble and I have a real gorging session, then let the puppies take the blame.

It always works. Just like pretending you aren't interested in a cuddle so that Ross will tickle, stroke and rub for hours at every bit of your furry little body. He needs to get a reaction from us: a purr, the louder the better, a turn on to the back with paws bent or a gentle lick of the fingers – he goes crazy for them, so all are forbidden until we've had enough.

I have come up with a kitten-training motto:

To get everything you want, just pretend you want nothing.

It works every time.

Burning
Question

5 November

It's not fair! Jenny said I had to stay in on November the fifth as it's too dangerous. She wouldn't tell me why, just that I wouldn't like what went on that day and night. Just because I'm gorgeous and cuddlesome she thinks I'm a scaredy cat. Well I'm not! I'm ferocious and tough. I can stand up to any marauding mouse.

I was thinking of ways to outsmart Jenny on that day (it's not hard) when the doorbell rang. I jumped up on to the windowsill to see who was visiting. It was some children I'd never seen before; they had a scruffy old doll in a creaky pram and they said something about forks. Jenny got her purse and gave them fifty pence but they didn't give her any forks. What a swizz. I tried to run after them when the door shut just in front of my whiskers. She meant it. I wasn't getting out. I sat howling on the mat for hours but she took no notice. 'It's for your own good Bluebell. You'd hate it.'

Bramble, Willow, the kittens and the dogs Bracken and Clover weren't bothered, they were snuggled up around the inglenook.

I found Jenny in the kitchen surrounded by sausages and trays of jacket potatoes. I tried to ask her what it was I'd hate so much that I had to miss my daily scoot up the apple tree. She took no notice but just stepped over me as she wrapped a woolly scarf around her neck. I jumped on to

the bench to sniff the sausages. She noticed me then all right. I was scooped up and bounced upstairs to the front bedroom. She shut me in!

I was furious until I saw the dish of chicken bits on newspaper. She loves me after all! I had a good tuck in and an even better lick. I settled down on the windowsill; the garden was dark and I longed to be out pouncing on every rustle. Then I panicked. Next door's garden was on fire! Great big flames lighting up the faces of every neighbour who'd rushed there to help. But what was going on? No one was trying to put the fire out. They were all smiling and warming their hands. The flames lit up Jenny's face. She was handing sausages around as if it was a party not a disaster.

I saw a filthy man with straw sticking out of his arm; he was wearing the old jeans and jumper Ross paints in. He was on top of the fire. I thought he'd get off when the flames reached his legs but no; he just sat there grinning. The jeans went up a treat. That means no more decorating for us.

Everyone turned away from the fire. I thought they'd seen sense and would run for buckets of water, but no! They were watching the bottom of the wall from where great sparks and coloured fires were whooshed into the dark sky. Through the double glazing I could hear faint bangs and screams of delight.

It was horrible, dangerous and mad – like most things humans did. Jenny could have stayed here in the warmth, sharing her supper with me.

She was right, I did hate it and so would anything with whiskers.

I have the Fifth clearly in my mind for next year. I won't have to be asked twice to stay in.

On second thoughts, I'd better make a bit of fuss; that chicken was delicious.

Demolition Day

19 November – 17 December

We've had some visitors. I thought they'd be no bother but, as Jenny says, children will be children. What a lot of stuff those little people bring with them. They said they couldn't live without toys for a week so not only did they take over two bedrooms but the dining room as well.

I stayed out of the way I can tell you. All that screeching and tearing around.

I wondered how the puppies' ears stayed on. Willow and Bramble had their tails stood on sixteen times. The kittens found sanctuary from stomping feet under Jenny's bed and stayed there. As always, I was cleverer than them. I managed to be in a different room to those hooligans every minute of the day. One morning, after they'd charged around the kitchen knocking jars and dropping crumbs, I had to flee into their bedroom. There was a TV, video and computer games, some dopey-looking cuddly toys and a little house.

I say little, but it was bigger than me and just like a real house with a roof and chimney and everything, only it had no glass in the windows. I know because I slid my paw in up to my chest. I could feel things in the rooms.

I withdrew my paw and put my eye right up to the windows so I could see inside. You wouldn't believe it, there was a table and chairs, a little fridge and cooker and the tiniest cat basket you ever did see. I tried another window. There was a tiddly man in a bed with a stiff-looking duvet so I stuck in my claw and hoisted him up, dropping him only once before hooking him clean out of the window. Lazy lump. What was he doing in bed before lunch?

I sank down to look in at the living-room window. I saw an unbending woman staring at a photograph of Princess Diana stuck to a pink plastic television set. Did she not realise it wasn't plugged in? I hooked her out for her plain stupidity.

In the little play room there was a whole host of blank-looking children failing to play snap with some cards bigger than themselves. I just biffed them to bits. Then I jiggled every bit of furniture in the house around. Revenge was sweet.

When the rowdy visitors returned from making the horse's life a misery they screamed and cried at the destruction of their favourite toy. Jenny came in and was delighted.

'Now they know how it feels,' she said as she gathered me up most affectionately. 'Good girl Bluebell,' she said smiling and she dropped a kiss on my sweet little head.

When the visitors had gone, two days early, everyone cheered and said I was the best demolition expert ever.

That's the first time I've been praised for it.

Jenny swore, 'No more kids around here. Never again!' I was glad we agreed on something. If any more children whoop their way around my territory I will bite their bottoms.

It was quiet for two weeks, then it arrived – the letter. It was from Hong Kong. I don't know where Hong Kong is but it can't be far as Jenny gets take-away food from its restaurant and that only takes twenty minutes to arrive.

'Oh heaven!' she said smacking a kiss at the handwritten page.

It must have been a new menu.

'Bluebell, my brother is bringing his two little girls here for a week! Isn't it wonderful?' I made a face that showed her I didn't think so and neither should she!

'Oh don't be silly Bluebell. These aren't children, they're family!'

There was a difference?

I was given a new basket. Flowers filled the house and washing fluttered on the line.

I wondered why Jenny was cleaning the kitchen floor twice in one month.

That drawer in the dresser could hardly shut it was so full of sweeties.

I was asleep when the little tearaways arrived and surprisingly they went to bed too. Jet lag, Jenny said. From the take-away to Ha'penny Hollow?

When they got up in the morning I understood why Jenny had been so excited. One was chatty and ever so polite and the other one looked like Jenny, only quarter size and without the wrinkles. They were so sweet even I fell for them.

We all had to go on show.

Willow purred as she popped her head from her picnic basket and Bramble pretended to chew her ears. Dandelion was scared and whistled out through the cat-flap, the children tried to follow. Amelia and Sasha thought we were teddies with everlasting batteries. Farthing was lifted to the bench to demonstrate how sweet he was when he was drinking his 'milkies'. The children liked to count how many times his tongue went in and out, even though he drank fifty to the dozen and they could only count to five. He had his saucer filled so many times I heard his tummy slop as Jenny lifted him to the floor.

The puppies were so polite it made me wonder if they'd had a personality transplant. They sat whenever the four-year-old approached and allowed eighteen-month-old Sasha to cuddle them, even though she was smaller than them. They all toddled off together.

When they came in from the snow they were cold and glowing. My basket was warm and inviting. Both girls tried to get in with me. I have never been partial to icy toes and fingers so I got out. They spent the rest of the afternoon in there sailing down the river to Africa.

I made the mistake of sauntering past on my way to the biscuits. I was grabbed round the middle and plopped on to my cushion. In their minds the boat had become a bed and I was to have a bedtime story read to me. They arranged a tea-towel over me and kissed me goodnight. I didn't enjoy the story because they couldn't read but they told me what the 'pichurs' were all about. I just complied. I had never seen anything like it.

When they went it felt peaceful but boring. I couldn't settle. Nothing will ever seem quite the same again.

I'm off for a sail in my basket. Africa made the girls so happy it must be better than here. Maybe I'll see them there.

House Tree

19 December

They're at it again. I for one think it is daft. All those dangly things and shiny bits and what for? To hang on a tree . . . in the sitting room for heaven's sake.

Now I ask you, why should a tree in the house be any different to a tree in the garden? No reason, right? So why do my ears get blasted with a scream when I do the perfectly normal thing? Trees are meant to be explored. Climbing trees is what cats do. Nobody stops me clawing my way to the top of that other tree with dangly bits, in fact they cheer when I'm near the top. 'Knock those plums down Bluebell, those big juicy ones we can't reach.'

No, for some reason I'm not even to look at the house tree. Too tempting, Jenny says. Well they don't know everything. One year, when the house was full of visitors and they'd all gone mad singing about Jingle Bells and Silent Nights (it wasn't very silent that night with all their wailing), I curled myself around the base of that tree. It was a bit bright with all those silly flashing lights but they also made it warm. I stayed there until I knew the turkey was on its own in the kitchen. No one noticed or cared, they were all surrounded by empty bottles and paper hats and had boxes of chocolates on their fat tummies.

Somebody asked if they'd been to church this year, and they all said 'of course'. What was this church thing that only appeared once a year and where was it for the rest of the time? In the woods with the house tree?

I have to be good this Christmas as Jenny said I'd be in

a mince pie if I wasn't. I'm not to beat up any of the presents when everyone is sleeping. 'Even if it *is* boring old tartan slippers again,' she said, shooting a sideways glance at Ross.

I know from experience that once Jenny has a big glass of that sherry stuff she won't know or care what I do. She'll smile widely when I dash and tear at the discarded wrapping paper. Take my photo sixteen times as I gently pat a bauble on the lower branches of the house tree. Put silly paper hats on Bramble, Willow and the puppies, and drape the kittens in tinsel hoping to get a good photo this year of 'all her babies'. Then she'll make her babies sick with all the food she's bought too much of. But you know, I have high hopes that this year will be different as her final words last year, when she looked fit to burst and threw out rather a lot of bottles, were 'Never again'.

But I hope it won't be too different. We all get lots of love and tasty bits, and besides I saw a box of new dangly things, even bigger and brighter than before. Maybe I can break my record for the loudest crash yet.

Christmas
Hair-do

23–24 December

What a Christmas I'm going to have!
Usually all us little darlin's get smothered in presents and delicious food we never see again for the rest of the year. This time Jenny is being tough.

'Right Bluebell, I'm sick of being the only one around here to stretch my brain and my purse to make a wonderful festive week for you lot. This year it's my turn. Unless you come up with some pretty nifty presents for Ross and me, I'm cancelling Christmas!'

How could she? I don't even know where the shops are, and even if I did I don't have any of those little plastic cards Ross keeps cutting in half with the scissors. Where does money come from? Ross is always telling Jenny it doesn't grow on trees and he's right; I look every week just in case he's wrong.

I shot up the chestnut tree to search for the town centre. I was pleased to say I couldn't see it, though I looked in every field. I wasn't bothered as Jenny says it is such a crush at this time of year, and I'd just given myself an hour's hair-do, which I wouldn't want spoiled.

That gave me an idea.

As I can't buy presents I could give my services. Jenny loves a new hair style for Christmas and Ross is always looking like a haystack. I knew I could lick them into shape.

I waited until they were asleep so they would have a nice surprise when they woke up. There was lots of snoring when I jumped lightly on to the duvet. Jenny would be first as she was on her back. I stuck out my tongue and lathered up. At first she giggled and I thought I'd be caught, but then she began dreaming again and I got a good half hour. I started at her forehead and licked straight up until I got a nice peak about six inches tall. After that it was easy to curl the tip so it looked like the sea about to break on the shore. Ross is always saying he likes wavy hair.

He turned over then and lay on his stomach. I had no choice but to work on his crown. He'd have to use a mirror to enjoy my Christmas present to him but it presented endless creative possibilities.

I know he likes flowers so I licked every bit of his hair into a chrysanthemum shape. I settled down then, pleased with my work, especially as when they woke they were going to a Christmas Eve breakfast at Ross's employer's posh house.

I thought the bed was on fire the way they were both screaming when they got up. They looked beautiful. That is if you overlooked the fact that Ross resembled a dandelion clock. Jenny ran to the big mirror, screamed again and then hit Ross hard.

'It wasn't me!' he cried holding his sore arm. 'It must have been you! Just look at the state of *my* hair!'

I sneaked out and left them to it.

They didn't like my Christmas present.

I was heartbroken. Worse still, it's one day to go and I still have no gifts for them. I have to think hard and quick.

I thought I could let them have a sleep on my cushion but knowing them they might like it too much and keep it. I padded over for a snuggle there myself and just let my brain wander for inspiration.

By the time they came back singing and wobbling all over the place, I had a row of lovely presents lined up beneath the tree.

'Bluebell! You are wonderful!' Jenny sang as she cuddled me close. 'I love that dried up half mouse you've been batting around the garden all year and the big ball of your hair you have so nicely shaped. But most of all I am delighted with the fluffy, scruffy toffee you must have spent hours fishing behind the fridge for.'

She proved her pleasure by giving Willow, Bramble, Clover, Bracken, the kittens and me the best cut of turkey and a parcel of treats.

I have a whole year to find out where money comes from. And I must search out those shops. My tongue is still aching. Some people just don't appreciate good art!